A HANDBOOK OF *Sailing Barges*

PRIDE OF IPSWICH, *from a photograph, by courtesy of Mr. R. Stimson. (Junr.).*

Frontispiece

A HANDBOOK OF *Sailing Barges*

EVOLUTION AND DETAILS OF
HULL AND RIGGING

F. S. Cooper

ILLUSTRATED BY JOHN CHANCELLOR

FOREWORD BY JOHN LEATHER

ADLARD COLES
8 Grafton Street, London W1

Adlard Coles
William Collins Sons & Co. Ltd
8 Grafton Street, London W1X 3LA

First published in Great Britain by
Adlard Coles 1955
Reprinted 1967
Facsimile reissue 1989

*A CIP catalogue record
for this book is available
from the British Library*

ISBN 0 229 64232 2

Printed in Great Britain

PUBLISHER'S NOTE

The text of the book has not been altered from the original. The Index of Barge Owners'
Bobs (or house flags) and the illustrations of them, the lists of Commercial Barges (active),
Auxiliary Sail, Motor Barges and the List of Barge Owners have been retained as published
in 1955 to provide a record of the spritsail barge fleet in its last years of commercial
activity.

Contents

Foreword

When it was first published in 1955 *A Handbook of Sailing Barges* provided the best compact reference to the design, construction, rig and handling, as well as the basic lore of the spritsail barges of south east England. It remains unsurpassed for succinct information on these fascinating vessels, which is not surprising as it was written and illustrated by two men who knew these craft well.

Fred Cooper spent his life in barges, and even before starting work was voyaging in them with his father and brothers. When 17 years old he became master of the sailing barge *Gazelle*. Command of five other sailing barges followed, the last, the *Persevere*, being converted to a motor vessel with Fred remaining her master. However, he found pleasure in skippering several restored sailing barges in the revived barge races of the 1940s to 1960s, and in 1963 published his *Racing Sailormen*, a history of the sailing barge matches.

John Chancellor came to know the spritsail barges when he served in them for a time as mate. There was usually only a crew of two; often an elderly skipper and a young subordinate. Both had to put their weight behind the job in these heavily rigged craft with their heavy anchoring arrangements and old fashioned cargo stowage. John Chancellor experienced the sailing barge world after 1945, when it still held out in trade against power because of post war conditions and the shortage of motor tonnage. But it was long past its peak of numbers from the 2090 spritsail barges working from the Thames and from Essex, Suffolk and Kent in 1907, or even the 1100 which were sailing in 1930. Motor transport steadily took their work. Nevertheless, it was a gloriously spectacular Indian summer for those of us who witnessed it. But by the early 1950s auxiliary motors were being installed as fast as possible in the surviving sound sailing barges. Against this background the book was written.

It is pleasing that this handbook has been reissued, as interest in these sailing barges remains strong and many which are described in this book as having been converted to power have since been rerigged and refitted to their former appearance and seem set to sail for many more years as pleasure or charter craft.

For their owners and crews and the many more who rejoice to see the tall brown sails of the barges, this book continues to have great practical value as a manual of the type. It is also an enduring memorial to the experience, knowledge and skills of its author and illustrator, both of whom knew the occasional glories, the constant hard work, the discomforts, the frequent disappointments and some of the satisfactions of the bargeman's life under sail.

John Leather, Fingringhoe, Essex, 1989

CHAPTER ONE

PART **1**

Historical

To those who travel the waters of the Thames Estuary, the rapid dwindling, especially during the post-war years, of the one time large fleet of sailing barges has become very apparent. The turn of the century, the hey-day of these business-like and yet in their way beautiful craft, saw just over 2,000 barges trading. From 1907, with 2,090 registered, the numbers slowly decreased to 1,650 by 1918, and 1,100 by 1930.

At the beginning of World War II 600 barges were still in active commission, but at the end of hostilities the number still trading had fallen to around 300.

Several reasons account for this. A large number of the barges were in use during the war as storage hulks and, lying afloat in the Medway, suffered the ravages of worm. Came too, in the early post-war years, the increasing influence of mechanical propulsion, giving those craft still in good condition a reasonable chance of survival in the rising demand for speedier transport.

The rising cost of upkeep of sails, spars and cordage, was another factor which influenced owners in converting their craft to power. The bigger coastwise trading barges fitting auxiliary engines, the smaller river craft generally being stripped of their gear and relying entirely on mechanical propulsion.

By the end of 1950 the fleet comprised 80 craft under sail alone, 41 with auxiliary engines, and 60 with motors only. It seems therefore, that power will undoubtedly take the place of sails, except perhaps in the special trades such as the carriage and storage of explosives, and the sight of a commercial sailing craft trading up and down the London River, the Medway, and to the outports of the Estuary will become increasingly rare.

During the post-war years, another fleet which includes both sail and auxiliary craft has become increasingly popular. This is the large number of craft converted to yachts. The idea is not original, as before World War I a few craft were

converted to sailing homes, notably W. L. Wylie's *The Four Brothers* built as the *New Zealand* in 1879 and renamed *Gwalia* in about 1907. She was again trading in the 1930's for Fraser & White in the Isle of Wight but now lies, a derelict house barge, at Bembridge.

Cyril Ionides' *The Golden Hope*, referred to as *Ark Royal*, in his book 'A Floating Home', was formerly the *G.A.M.C.* built in 1869. In the early 1920's, after several active sailing years, she became a house barge at Stambridge on the Roach, and was eventually broken up at Maldon in 1951. R. R. Horlock's *Volunteer*, built 1879 and converted by C. A. Badcock in 1914, continued as a yacht until the early 1930's and her last appearance in the Register appears to be in 1934 when she was owned by Camper & Nicholson.

During the early 1930's, when several barges were for sale, as little as £50. could purchase a craft capable of carrying as much as 100 tons of cargo. Naturally the idea of converting these craft to yachts and homes began to gain in popularity, and from then onwards the number converted steadily increased and although many laid up and deteriorated during the war years, 1949 saw several of these vessels in commission.

Whilst these conversions may not meet with the approval of the purists, they may yet be the means of keeping some of the barges in commission and, as several of their owners attempt to keep the exterior in general appearance as when the craft were trading, it should be possible to see the Thames Sailorman in the Estuary, and cruising the East and South Coasts, for some years to come looking much as they have done during the past half-century.

Some craft were actually built as barge yachts, *Mamgu* ex *Cawana* 1904 and *Daisie* 1907. Both were launched by Gill of Rochester, who

was responsible for *Dinah* in 1887, one of the earliest. Still afloat, *Dinah* is only half the average size with 45·3 length overall and 12·2 beam. Howard of Maldon built *Thoma II* in 1909 on the lines of their well-known ketch *Record Reign*. With her graceful clipper bow and counter stern, *Thoma II* is easily recognisable. Some idea of the overhang of this vessel can be gathered by comparing the waterline length of 81·9 feet with the deck length of 100 feet. Details of her scrollwork are illustrated in a later chapter.

Sea Gull II, an ex War-Department owned barge is the smallest topsail barge now in commission as a barge yacht. Even smaller, with a cargo capacity of only 20 tons, is the tiller steering stumpy-rigged *Rainbow*, now wintering on the River Lea at Clapton. She was built at Berkhampstead in Surrey in 1901 for trading between the various farms on the banks

9

of the Crouch and Roach and her owner's mill at Battlesbridge. *Rainbow* traded until the early thirties and was to be seen off Leigh-on-Sea until just before World War II, when she was fitted with a new suit of sails.

A few small yachts have been built on barge lines. Two of the best known on the Medway and the East Coast today are *Nancy Grey* and *Dione*, both launched from the Shuttlewood yard at Paglesham. They have both given a very good account of themselves in the small barge yacht class races sailed on the Medway annually since 1949, *Nancy Grey* leading her bigger sisters home in 1950-51-52. These craft are cutter rigged with a sail area of just over 500 sq. ft. and both craft have almost identical hull measurements: *Nancy Grey*, length 30·1 feet with 9·3 ft. beam and *Dione*, 30·5 ft. by 9·1 ft. The latter draws as little as 1·7 ft. and the former 2 ft., in both cases with the lee-boards up.

1. *The little* CYGNET, *l.o.a. 41 ft., beam 13 ft., registered tons 13. Built at Frindsbury in 1881 for trade in the rivers Stour and Orwell.*

11

2. *Swim heads and Budget sterns.*

CHAPTER TWO

Evolution of Hull and Rig

THE modern barge developed slowly from the box-like craft of the 18th century, whose hull form is perpetuated in the present day lighters that deal with so much of the London River Transhipment work. These early barges with swim heads and budget sterns, were entirely open, but by 1809 decks were fitted and hatch covers made for the one large hold.

The round bow began to supersede the swim head from 1840, leading to the straight stem of the end of the century. The transom stern came after 1860 and the sailing barge was very much as seen today, but with very square section and little or no run at the ends.

The introduction of the Sailing Matches by William Henry Dodd in 1863 and the keen competition that developed from these races during the next 25-30 years, gave incentive to the improvement of hull lines, so that by 1895-1900 the barge yards were busy dealing with orders for craft that were fast and able to deliver cargoes beyond the river limits.

Piper of Greenwich built the famous *Giralda*, thought by many to be the fastest barge ever.

Her record in the Sailing Matches is certainly imposing: champion of the Thames 1898-1900, 1904-5, 1908, fifth 1902—after damaging her gear, fourth 1903 and third 1906. Champion on the Medway 1898, 1900, 1903 and 1904, disqualified 1905, second 1897, 1899 and third 1903. One wonders how she would fare with *Veronica*, *Sara* and others of the later racing

3. *Round Bow*.

periods. Other barges from the Piper Yard were *Surf*, *Surge*, *James Piper*, *Ernest Piper*, *Haughty Belle* and *Leonard Piper* in 1910.

The Harwich and Ipswich Yards were also busy at this time with their own type of hull, and although these craft, having to face the Estuary all their trading days and sometimes long coastal passages, were heavier lined, they had a beauty of their own, and the barges from the Cann Yard (see Fig. 5) are regarded by most bargemen to be nearest to perfection, being generally fast, sea-kindly and having good stowage space. *Felix*, *Kitty*, *Centaur*, *Ethel*, *Memory* and *May* are the sailing survivors of the Cann Yard, with *Edith May*, *Leofleda*, *Kimberley*, *Gladys* and *Beric* active as auxiliaries.

The Howard-built barges from Maldon, engaged mostly in stack work from the Essex farms generally situated at the head of a narrow creek, were given a much shallower and beamier

4.   LEFT. *An early transom form, following the Budget stern.* RIGHT. *A later period showing the broadening trend towards the present day.*

hull, but lacked nothing in looks and could easily be identified amongst the Estuary craft. Several of these barges finished their lives as yacht barges and, although some of them are now house boats stripped of their gear, three are still sailing as yachts, namely, *Violet* (see Fig. 5), built 1889, *Saltcote Belle* 1895, and *Venta* (see Fig. 6), originally *Jachin* 1893.

Wooden barges were being built up to 1928 when *Cabby* was launched from the London and Rochester Barge Co.'s Yard at Frindsbury. Converted to auxiliary in 1931, *Cabby* formed part of the fleet which sailed to the Clyde during the second World War, working as far North as the Outer Hebrides at one time and returning at the end of hostilities to her normal trading. As well as the last wooden barge to be built, *Cabby* is the last of the long line of barges to be built by the family of Gill, who started building on the Medway in 1858.

Among other builders during the 1920's was Hutson of Maidstone, builder of the auxiliaries *Marie May*, *Scone*, *Thyra*, the motor barge *Mousmé*, and also of *Rosmé* another mine victim in the West Swin.

Short Bros. of Rochester built the fine coasting barges *Lady Jean*, *Lady Daphne*, and *Lord Haig* 1930. *Lady Jean* and *Lady Daphne* both built in 1923, are still trading as auxiliaries for R & W. Paul of Ipswich. *Lady Daphne* will be remembered for the remarkable way in which she survived the Channel Gale of December, 1928. Bound for Fowey from Weymouth, she was attempting to make Plymouth for shelter in a N.E. gale and heavy snow squalls, when her Skipper was lost overboard and her sails, with the exception of the bowsprit jib, were blown away. Her crew were taken off after a 12-mile chase by the Lizard life-boat. The abandoned barge sailed through Crow Sound in the Scillies

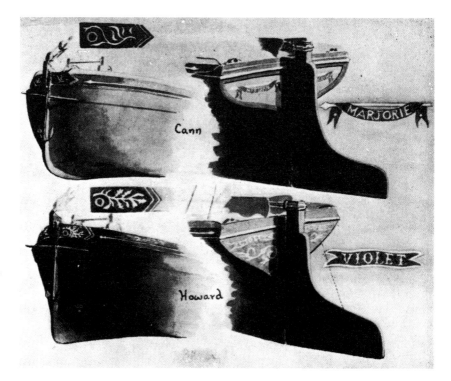

5.

ABOVE. *The bow and stern of* MARJORIE *showing the full convex form of the Cann barges.*

BELOW. *The bow and stern of Howard's* VIOLET, *a typical example of his graceful concave treatment.*

6. *Originally named* JACHIN, VENTA *shown resting on barge blocks, is an excellent example of Howard's artistry.*

and beached herself on Tresco. Three days later she was salvaged, towed to Hugh Town and finally to the mainland for refit.

Lord Haig was sunk after a collision with a trawler off the Humber.

Wills & Packham of Sittingbourne, already responsible for the building of several river barges, launched during the early 20's the crack *Phoenician*, winner of 9 first and 1 second prizes in 10 races. Other craft from this yard although not so well known for their speed were fine sea-going vessels. *Olive Mary*, built 1921, renamed *Arcades* and converted to auxiliary power 1938, met an untimely end by being burnt down to the water outside Sheerness, June 11th, 1947, whilst loaded with straw for the Paper Mills at Ridham Dock. *Raybel*, built 1920, is still active as an auxiliary on the East Coast, as well as *Olive May*, launched as a motor barge in 1920.

The yards of the White family, the son at Conyer and at Faversham, and the elder White at Sittingbourne from the early 1890's until 1910, launched several fast craft. *Sara* came from the Conyer Yard during 1901. The last barge built there was *Joy* in 1914. Several other fast craft, among them *Nelson*, *Queen*, *Satanita*, *Vectis*, *Clara* and *Victoria*, were from the Sittingbourne Yard. *Beatrice Maud*, launched in 1910 and still trading under the Sully flag as an auxiliary, was the last to leave the ways on Alfred White's yard.

The most prolific of the builders were the Shrubsall family, building 15 barges between 1895 and 1901 at Ipswich and 13 at Limehouse and Greenwich, with one other, *Veravia*, rebuilt by them in 1925. An earlier branch of the family built at Milton near Sittingbourne during the 1880's. All the Shrubsall barges were fast and had very little sheer. The Milton craft having fine long runs aft and forward, were notoriously wet in any sort of sea-way with their lack of sheer, but the Ipswich and London built barges had longer chines and rounder ends. *Veronica* from the London Yard, with 12 firsts and 1 second place in 13 starts, was Queen of this fleet, but several others of this build were noted racing craft, prizewinners including *Genesta*, *Verona*, *Valdora* and *Imperial*. *Violet Sybil*, *Sirdar* and *Mildreda* were from the Ipswich yards.

Other well known Ipswich builders included Orvis & Fuller, Bayley, Curtis, Robertson, Peck, and R. & W. Paul, and at Harwich, Maclearon, Norman, and Cann. Other equally well known builders were Horlock at Mistley, Stone at Brightlingsea, Cook at Maldon, Kemp & Shuttlewood at Paglesham, and Rose at Shoeburyness, with Everard, Keep, Miller & Goldsmith on the Thames. Apart from the Kentish builders mentioned previously, other

well known firms were Smeed, Dean & Co., Eastwoods Ltd., Taylor, Cremer, Goldfinch, and The Whitstable Shipping Co. Going a little further afield, we have R. & T. Smith at Rye, Harvey at Littlehampton, renowned for ketch rigged barges, and Henry Felton added his quota from Sandwich. On the Medway, apart from the Gill family, other yards were owned by Wakeley Bros., G. F. Curel, A. J. Knight, and James Little of Borstal, builder of the well-known *Glen* barges.

The longevity of barges is a by-word and *Favorite*, built 1803, is still afloat. Originally swim head and budget sterned, the latter was altered to a transom after being in collision in 1870 and the swim head gave way to the straight stem in 1899. *Favorite* traded until the early 1930's and then became a yacht barge until the outbreak of War. Unrigged, she now lies at Hammersmith as a house barge.

20

The oldest trading barge today under sail is *George Smeed*, launched by Smeed, Dean & Co. at Murston in 1882 and rebuilt by them in 1922. Several barges are still trading that were built before 1890. *Gipping*, still under sail, was launched at Ipswich in 1889. *Ethel Maud*, Maldon built in 1889 is the oldest commercial auxiliary. Several veterans are amongst the barges converted to yachts, *British Lion* 1876, *Violet* 1889, *Lord Churchill*, *Mayland* and *Mermaid* all built 1888. *Persevere* from Sittingbourne 1889, is still trading as a motor barge.

Steel began to be used in a number of hulls built by E. J. & W. Goldsmith of Grays, ranging from 100 ton capacity 'stumpies' built at their own yard, 1900, to the 150 and 180 ton class as built by J. G. Fay & Co. at Southampton, 1898-9 and, during the same period, the 155 ton

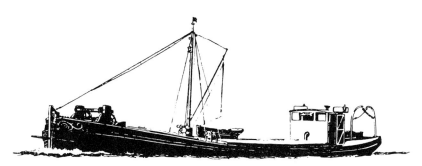

7. PERSEVERE, *stripped of her gear and relying on power alone.*

21

class by Brabey & Co. at Deptford. 1903-4 saw the big 280 ton capacity barges built at Krimpen D'Ysel by Otto & Zonen, and at Papendrecht by Kievits & Van Reede.

The well known 280 ton *Will*, *Ethel*, *Alf*, and *Fred Everard* were from the yard of Fellowes & Co. at Great Yarmouth in 1926, the firm which, in 1898, was responsible for the crack *Fortis*. *Thistle* the only Thames barge to be built in Scotland came from the yard of Hamilton & Co. at Port Glasgow. *Mafeking* and *Adriatic* also started their careers a long way from the Thames, as both were built at Beverley in Yorkshire by J. Scarr & Co. The *Adriatic* shows a strong family likeness to the Keels.

During the 1920's, Piper's of Greenwich were building steel craft but, with the exception of *Pip* and *Wilfred*, they concentrated on motor craft and lighters.

Aldous & Co. of Brightlingsea, launched in

1924, two big steel barges of 280 tons capacity for R. & W. Paul of Ipswich. Both these barges were left on the beaches at Dunkirk, but one, *Aidie*, is still afloat in Dunkirk as a coal hulk.

The last steel sailing barges to be built came from the Mistley Yard of F. W. Horlock & Sons in 1930. *Resourceful*, converted to motor in 1933, and *Blue Mermaid*, who met an untimely end by falling victim to a magnetic mine off the Hook Middle Buoy, near the Whitaker Spit in July, 1941.

Reminder, a noted racer of pre-war days, winner of her class in 1929, 1930 and 1934, came from this yard in 1929, as also did *Adieu*. Both are now power craft. Other steel craft from Horlocks' yard are *Portlight* 1925, *Repertor* 1924, and *Xylonite* in 1926.

*　　　*　　　*

The spritsail and leeboard are both of Dutch origin. The rig was certainly employed in

Holland as far back as 1416 and some of the early Thames barges had it by 1600. The rig developed slowly and, by the end of the 18th century, the usual sail plan still consisted of foresail and main, the latter a spritsail. Brails were used to stow the sail and consisted of a main brail secured at the nock on one side, led across the sail, round the leech, back across the other side of the sail, through a single block and down to the deck. There was also a peak and lower brail working on the same principle. (Fig. 9). In the modern sailing barge's mainsail, two peak brails are fitted on each side with standing parts fast to leech, led through blocks at head rope and mast head to the deck. The main brail consists of a hemp or chain strop through cringles in the leech, to which is attached a wire brail on either side; these lead through single blocks at nock and unite to a single wire leg leading to a winch on deck. The

23

8. PORTLIGHT, *built of steel.*

lower part of the sail is fitted with one or two brails according to the size of the sail, each made up of a single part of rope leading through a block at the luff, across the sail, through a cringle at the leech, across the other side of the sail, through a single block on this side at the luff, and both parts knotted clear of the luff and led to the deck. (Fig. 9).

The mainsheet in the early barges had the standing part fast in the clew, through a single block on the horse and another on the leech then back to make fast on the horse block. The increase in sail area in later barges gave rise to the need for extra purchase, and the modern style of a double block at the horse and an extra single block on the leech was evolved.

With the increasing length of hull an extra sail was needed to assist in handling and about 1800 mizzens were added. (Fig. 10). The mast was stepped on the rudder post and the sheet led from the boom through a block on the rudder blade, back through a block on the boom and belayed on the tiller. These sails were small and of little driving power but, with the fitting of wheel steering later, the mizzens were stepped in-board and made larger to balance the increased head sail of later craft, the maximum size being the big mule-rigged mizzens on some of the coast-wise traders. (Fig. 11).

Barges at the beginning of the 19th century began to extend their voyages beyond the usual river limits to the Estuary. Several of these were cutter rigged, but this rig had died out on the river by about 1860, although the coasting craft still carried on the gaff sail, generally as ketches or dandies. The bigger spritsail barges, as well as the cutters, were setting jibheaded topsails and in some craft a square topsail as well. The headstick of the modern topsail began to be used around 1890.

Brails, old & new

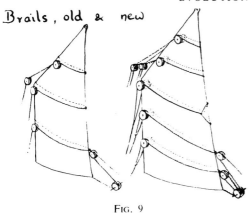

FIG. 9

The standing rigging up to 1890 had been made from tarred hemp but, after this date, wire began to be used and iron to replace the wooden tabernacles or mast box, caps, crosstrees and some of the blocks. Wheel steering also came into more general use, although *Anglo-Norman*

is reputed to have been fitted with wheel steering as early as 1882. Tillers, however, were still fairly common up to the early 1920's. *Eva Annie* built 1878, and *Diligent* built 1877, were the last in commission, the former trading under sail until 1933 with her tiller and a further six years wheel steered, whilst the latter finished up as a lighter in the timber trade on the Blackwater between Osea Island and Heybridge Basin. Several barges were still trading with the early 'Stumpy' rig until the middle 1930's, the last of these being *Emma* (Fig. 12), built 1899 and trading around the Thames and Medway until the early 1940's when, after losing her sprit and mainsail off Whitstable, she was laid up off Leigh-on-Sea. She is now under way as a motor yacht barge. One other stumpy barge, *Bessier*, converted to a yacht in 1933, spent the pre-war years in the Poole Harbour area and is now a derelict house barge at Weymouth.

25

As the barges began to travel farther afield so the builders began to develop the shape of the hull, the short, steep tide swell of the Estuary calling for better shaped ends with more sheer than was to be seen in the early river barges, also the influence of the Sailing Matches could be found in the under water lines, so that, where the hull form prior to 1890 had a flat deck line and very short almost abrupt runs at bow and stern, the long after run, finer bow entry and long easy sheer of the typical Estuary barges of today began to emerge.

The particular trade of the barges, too, had a good deal to do with the hull form. The craft built for the hay and straw and other farm work in the days when traffic was horse-drawn, were given more beam and shallow sides. The beam was necessary to enable them to carry the enormous stacks stowed on deck from the farms in Essex or Suffolk to London, and as the farms

10. **DILIGENT,** *showing mizzen stepped on rudder post.*

11. *'Mule' rigged mizzen.*

were generally at the head of some tidal creek, a shallow draft was necessary.

Barges built in the Harwich and Ipswich yards were given deeper, more sea-kindly sides and more sheer fore and aft, smaller hatchways and wide, cambered decks. A number of these barges started their careers as ketch or boomie barges, giving way later to the more economical spritsail rig, but retaining the big gaff mizzen. The last sailing barge to have been so rigged was the yacht barge *Alice May*, built at Harwich 1898, but other sprit rigged barges have been given the mulie mizzen when built and *Cambria* and *Will Everard*, so rigged, are still trading commercially, the latter an auxiliary but still retaining a full sail plan. The yacht barges *Thoma II* and *Wolsey* also have gaff mizzens.

The Estuary barges were generally of heavier tonnage than river craft and, although plenty of barges traded in the Estuary that were of but

12. EMMA, *last of the 'stumpies'*.

100 tons capacity, the average size was around 120-140, tons with the coasters averaging 160-180 tons. The maximum size was reached in the four *Everards*, the Dutch-built Goldsmith barges, and R. & W. Paul's *Barbara Jean* and *Aidie*, built at Brightlingsea 1924. These two last named craft had but a short sailing life, ending their trading days on the beaches of Dunkirk, as mentioned.

The river trading barges were generally of flat sheer, and capacity was a more important factor than speed, though many of them turned out to be quite fast. The smallest, known as Cut barges, trading to the Regent and the Surrey Canals, with an average capacity of 70-80 tons and as little as 14 ft. beam, were generally stumpie rigged, and were handy and fast with their high peaked mainsail. They had the least sheer of any barge, being designed for this special trade where, beside a narrow beam being essential, the vessel had to pass under low bridges and could not afford any sheer. These cut barges when working the Canals had to stow the lee-boards on deck, and have the anchor on deck and the dinghy too, to find room in some of the locks and, with their gear lowered flat on deck, the highest part of the vessel would be the wheel, from which the spokes could be removed to gain another few inches. Even this would not allow passage back light on some canals, and the barge had to be partially flooded to get under the bridge or tunnel and be pumped out after passing through.

The large number of brickfields in Kent and Essex employed fleets of barges of about 100 tons capacity, with fairly box-like sections to make for easy stowage. These craft, having to work mainly in either a narrow creek or congested river, were generally very handy to manoeuvre. A 100 ton barge would stow on an average 40-42,000 bricks.

CHAPTER THREE

PART **2**

Construction

THE building of barges was a craft handed down from one generation to another. The products of the shipwright's skill and workmanship live on, and no-one can deny the durability of the barge hull which must be one of the strongest hull forms ever evolved. Few loaded craft could recover from strains involved when overhanging a shelf with only part of the hull supported, or from stranding across a narrow channel as in the case of the *Emma* in this sketch 13 taken from a photograph. She is shewn sitting across the narrow channel through the mud flats off Leigh-on-Sea, in September, 1935. In this instance although the barge failed to lift on the first tide, she was refloated on the next and all that was necessary to put her into commission again was re-spiking all over. *Emma* was active commercially until the early 1940's and is still under way, as mentioned earlier, as a motor yacht barge. Other barges have bent almost as far in the other direction and lived to trade again. These accidents generally left some weakness in the structure and such berths were not used from choice, yet they show the great strength and resilience of the barge hull.

The shipwrights responsible for the building of these wonderful craft belong to the age of the adze and the saw pit when all the timber was shaped by hand and one can but marvel at the skill and workmanship that went into each part of the hull. There was, too, a plentiful supply of good English oak and other seasoned timber, which attributed much to the longevity of these vessels.

Another remarkable feature of the building of these craft was that whereas most craft were built from lines and detailed blue prints, the general practice at the barge yards was to prepare a half model and the foreman ship-wright would take the measurements he wanted from this, and for the rest depend on his eye and craftsmanship.

This pecularity would account for the indivi-duality found in craft launched from the various yards, each builder expressing his own theory regarding the particular type of barge with which he was concerned, whether the vessel was the big coaster or the river trader, whether designed for speed or for the ability to carry as much cargo as possible on the least draught, to name but a few of the special points that the owner wanted incorporated in the new hull.

As in all other craft, the first part of the structure to be laid was the keel; this consisted of a shallow baulk of elm averaging about 14 inches in width, with a depth of $4\frac{1}{2}$ inches and running the full length of the hull. The stem with its apron and knee and the stern post and knee were next bolted to the keel at respective ends and the sternframe of 6 inches by 12 inches oak fastened to the sternpost. This part of the hull varied in shape considerably with some builders, some preferring a deep rounded form as in the case of Shrubsall, whilst Howard favoured a

13. EMMA, *stranded across Leigh Creek, September 1935, from a photograph by courtesy of Mr. R. Stimson Jnr.*

V-shape, Cann favoured a more tucked-up sternframe, as did the other Harwich builder Maclearon. The scroll work and name ribbons on the transom varied with each builder and in some cases could be regarded as a trade mark. The sterns illustrated show some of the most individual types both in shape and fancywork.

Maclearon barges had a most distinctive shape and scrollwork, *Alice May* being a typical example of craft built on this yard before 1901 and *Ena* showing the style in use in 1906.

Cann, another of the Harwich builders, favoured the transom form shown in the sketch of *Felix*, and the name ribbon is typical of all the stern decorations of the Cann built barges.

Howard, the Maldon builder from 1879-1909, favoured the V-shape shown in the *Violet* stern. The scroll, although following the same general shape in the main stem of the design used on Howard transoms, shows a good deal of variety

in the additions to this stem. A few of the Howard barges such as *Defender* and *D'Arcy* had a ribbon draped over a spear and daffodils in the scrollwork on the bow, attributed to the handiwork of the crippled son of the builder. Another distinctive feature of the decoration was the particular style of lettering. The deep transom of the Shrubsall barges carried little in the way of decoration but the surround of the name is typical of all. A few built at Ipswich had a small scroll added but usually the transom was left very sparsely decorated, as in the case of *Mildreda*.

The bottom of the barge was the next to be built, and consisted generally of 3 in. Oregon Pine planking, rabbetted together and the joints filled with tar and cow hair. In some cases a double skin of $1\frac{1}{2}$ in. planking was used, but in either method the peculiar arrangement known as bottom screw was employed to draw

33

the bottom planking together. This bottom screw consisted of chains and a large screw at one end, the screw being tightened at intervals to squeeze out the surplus tar from between the planking to make the bottom watertight.

The floor timbers, varying in size according to the size of the barge (between 6-8 inches by 5 inches in craft of 100 tons capacity and as much as 12 inches by 7 inches in larger craft), were next fastened to the bottom planking with oak trenails, so shaped that when driven home they formed a tight and strong fastening. The frames were halved on to the floor timbers (Fig. 16), and at the bows bolted to the deadwood and given an angle to follow the line of the bow. These upright frames were strutted temporarily in position whilst the outer planking was offered up. The side planking, of 3 inch oak, if single skin was favoured or, more usually, two skins each of 1½ inch thickness, were next

34

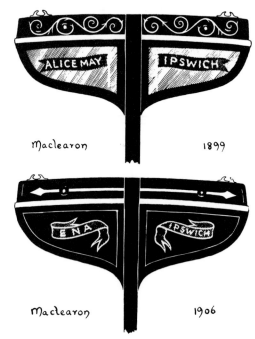

Fig. 14. Scroll work and name ribbons.

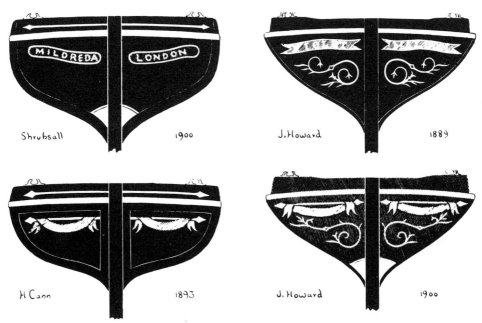

Fig. 15. Scroll work and name ribbons.

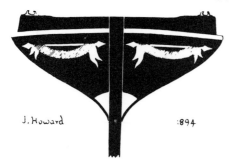

J. Howard   1894

Smead Dean   1889

Fig. 15—continued.

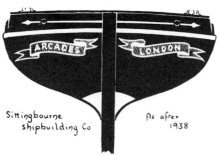

Sittingbourne
Shipbuilding Co   As after 1938

fitted. As in the bottom planking, each plank was rabbetted and tar and cow hair used in the joints. The top plank of the side, the outer wale, was of oak and generally nearly twice the thickness of the side planking, with a depth of just over 12 inches but sometimes as deep as 18 inches. The lower plank or chine was of similar dimensions, with chine keelsons of around 13 inches by 6 inches fitted and bolted inside the frames at the junction of floors and frames. The main keelson, the backbone of the barge, was originally always of timber and in some craft an Oregon Pine baulk up to 18 inches square reaching the length of barge was used. This member lay on the floors and was through-bolted to the keel, with the ends scarphed to the deadwood at stem and stern. Above the chine keelson came the lining of 2 inch pitch pine, with the inner wale of 3 inch by 14-18 inch oak running right round the sides above the lining. The mainbeams and deck carlings rested on the inwale and were fastened to the uprights, varying in size from the sailing beams in way of the mast case of 8-9 inches square, to the carlings of 5-6 inches by 4 inches. All were of oak, with a support under the mast case from the main keelson, of a 10 inch square baulk. Other heavy deck beams were fitted at the after end of the main hatch, under the forward end

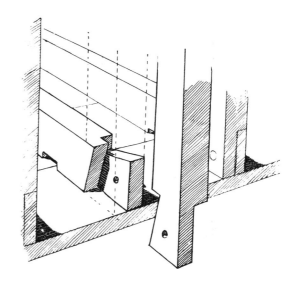

16. *The jointing of floors and frames
at the chine.*

37

of the cabin top, and also at the forward end of forehold and beyond. The smaller carlings were fitted under the decks with filling pieces between the carlings made removable to allow inspection of the framework. In some barges these filling pieces were hinged but this was not usual.

A tie beam was built in to most barges across the width of vessel midway along the main hold, but in others this was made removable to facilitate the stowage of cargoes such as timber. When this was done, a chain with a tension screw was fitted across the hold to prevent the sides sagging outwards.

In some later barges the deck beams and carlings were often of steel and in a good many craft the wooden keelsons were taken out and replaced by steel girders of T or H section. This change made for a saving in space but, not having the natural spring of the timber keelsons, were not as satisfactory as the originals.

38

Some craft had three main keelsons of steel of smaller dimensions which barely protruded above the $2\frac{1}{2}$ inch Oregon or Pitch pine ceiling. This ceiling, fitting between the main and chine keelsons and covering the floor of the cargo space, was spiked to the floor timbers with the exception of the second plank from the chine keelsons and running the entire length of the hold. This was made removable to allow access to the channels through the floors and thus enable the bilges to be cleared of any rubbish that may have found its way through. The channels, or limber holes, were to allow a free passage of bilge water to the pumps. *McKinley* and *Unique*, the latter built at Sittingbourne 1903, were of composite construction with metal framework and wooden skin.

Iron hanging knees were fitted at strategic points, passing under the deck beams, down the lining, and sometimes continuing across the ceiling, bolted to the floors and frames. Other strengthening features incorporated in the structure were the breast hook in the eyes of the vessel securing the inwales and apron, and grown oak lodging knees fitted and bolted at the angles of the beams. Occasionally, diagonal iron straps were fitted inside the frames and floors to give additional strength.

During the barge's lifetime it was usual to have to add another skin, or 'double' the hull, and some had more than one such extra skin. Some barges were 'boxed', as this operation was generally called, fairly early in their life, but others went for many years before needing this attention, depending on their trade and the berths they had to use. Iron bands, $2\frac{1}{2}$-3 inches wide were fastened round the outside edges of the covering boards and often to the lower edge of the wales as protection. A leeboard head chock or striker was bolted to the side, or suspended by chains, forward of the leeboard to protect the leading edge or head of the leeboard, when sliding alongside other craft or a quay.

Steel barges were of simpler construction and having lighter frames than the wooden craft had better cargo space. These craft had no lining in the holds and the ceiling was practically clear of any obstruction, having only a small sectioned main keelson. The angle of side and bottom was well rounded, as too was the fore-foot in the Southampton-built barges, but the later Mistley craft had harder chine sections, and followed the traditional hull shape more closely, which may have accounted for the speed of *Reminder*, *Portlight* and others from this yard. Rudders were generally made of steel, but some builders such as Scarr of Beverley, Brabie of Deptford, and Fellowes of Yarmouth, fitted wooden rudders. Leeboards were still of timber and occasionally decks were covered with

39

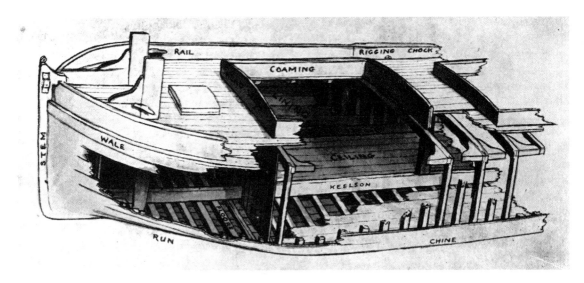

17. *Cut away forward section.*

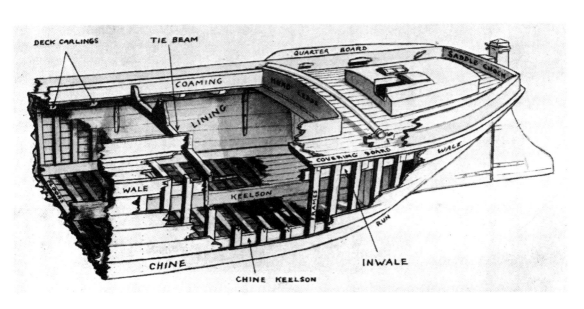

18. *Cut away aft section.*

planking, but otherwise steel was used throughout. Many steel craft have passed the half-century and are still trading, but as motor craft. The last steel commercial sailing barge over 50 years of age was *Carina* unrigged December, 1952, but a sister to this barge, *Scotia*, was converted to a yacht barge, being still under sail during 1952, and commercially employed as a lighter at Maldon in 1953.

On deck the first and most important planking to be laid was the covering board of oak, 3 inches thick and up to 12 inches wide, laid round the outer edge of the deck above the junction of beams and frames. Inboard of this, the planking was usually of 6 inches by 3 inches pitch pine, each plank shaped in the usual way to give an $\frac{1}{8}$ inch caulking seam. This was caulked and payed with pitch to make the whole watertight.

CHAPTER FOUR

Hatchways and Cargo Space

THE hatch coamings were then fitted, the fore and aft sections standing on the inboard strake of the deck and the thwartship members, or 'headledges', standing on deck above the main beams. The size of the barge's hatchway varied considerably; in the big coasting craft, wide decks and small hatchways were usual, a great advantage in a sea-way but not making the stowing of cargo very easy. The river barges, generally working in more sheltered waters and designed more for handiness in working cargo, had narrower decks and pro-portionately larger hatchways, some, such as *Ninety-Nine*, *Alumina* and *Busybody*, had as little as 15-18 inch wide main decks. These craft were exceptional and designed for mud cargoes to be used in the manufacture of cement, but the average deck width for 100 ton barges was 24-30 inches. The height of the coamings varied considerably from 12-14 inches in the river craft to over 2 feet in larger craft. In craft dealing with cargoes of high specific gravity the space enclosed in hold and hatchway would be ample to store their cargoes below hatches, but in

43

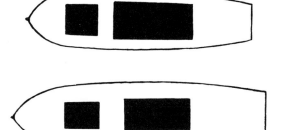

19. *Above. The large hatchways of the river barge compared with the proportionately small openings of the coaster (below).*

Inside the coamings a ledge was fitted to the fore and aft members to support the hatch carlings, with a socket of wood or steel inside the thwartship coamings in which the fore and aft hatch beams seated.

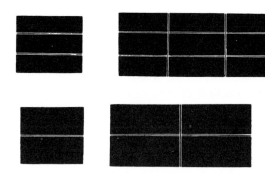

20. *Above. The usual arrangement of hatch beams to be found on large coastal barges.*

Below. The common arrangement for river craft.

some trades, such as the carriage of grain, etc., extra space in the hatchways would be needed, as few barges could load to maximum draught without carrying some of the cargo above hatch level. The coamings were 4-5 inches in thickness and gave additional lateral strength to the hull.

44

General practice was to have these hatch beams running along the centre of the hatchway with a socket on the main tie beam, or hatch beam in craft using this latter beam in conjunction with the chain tie mentioned earlier, but in some larger craft double thwart hatch beams were fitted with double fore and aft beams. All these were removable for handling cargo. The main coamings were generally shaped down at the forward end to allow the mast to be lowered without interfering with the hatchway, but in barges with high coamings it was usual to make a section of the forward thwartship member of the main coaming removable to allow the mast to lower. It was also necessary to remove a few of the forward main hatches in these barges and care had to be taken that water did not get down on to the cargo whilst the hatchway was opened and hatch cloths had to be arranged in the best way possible.

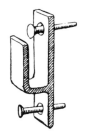

21. *Batten hook.*

Where the after end coaming ran close to the mainhorse it was sometimes found necessary to shape the coamings down to suit, but this only occurred in small craft. Around the outside of the coamings were the batten hooks of iron let in and drift bolted. Iron bands were fitted around the top of the coamings and also at the top of the hatch ledge inside the hatchway. Bulkheads of Oregon or Pitch pine were built to partition off the long hold from the cabin aft and the

45

forecastle forward, and were of double thickness $1\frac{1}{2}$ inch planking.

Many barges also had an iron band running round the lower edge of the hatchway, depending mainly on the particular trade of the barge and the amount of banging about from crane grabs to which the coamings were likely to be exposed.

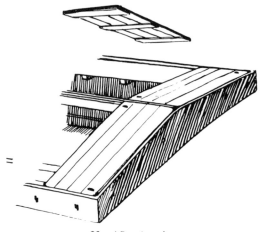

23. '*Dominoes*'.

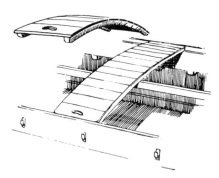

22. *The usual cambered hatches.*

To complete the covering of the cargo space, hatches (generally of a standard pattern 18-24 inches in width) were added. Each hatch consisted of two oak carlings 3 or 4 inches by $2\frac{1}{2}$

46

inches cut with a camber, with $\frac{3}{4}$ to 1 inch soft wood boards nailed across and elm hand boards at either end. (Fig. 22). The average number of hatches fitted to a 100 ton barge would be 15 on the mainhold and 4-5 forward, and to 130-140 ton craft, 18 on 20 on the mainhold. Occasionally flat hatches, known to bargemen as 'dominoes' (Fig. 23), were fitted and consisted of deal plank-ing made up to 18-24 inch widths and fitting between the hatch ledges and a ledge on the fore and aft beams. These were far less convenient when covering up, especially if time was limited.

Heavy hatch cloths tucked in the batten hooks, the battens of wood or iron put in and oak wedges driven home, completed the closing of the hatchways.

CHAPTER FIVE

Rails and Deck Fittings

BOLTED down to the covering board and set inboard 4-5 inches were the rails. These varied in height considerably with the craft. River barges usually had rails of about 8 inches by 3 inches, amidships, rising generally to 12 inches or so at the stem, and about 10 inches aft. Scuppers were cut out at intervals to allow water to run off the deck. Quarter boards were added aft varying in height and shape and generally with a capping piece of 1½ inch oak. A capping piece would sometimes be added on the rail forward of the fore horse. The badge boards were added just abaft the stem and right aft and, with the names carved on the bow and a streak cut round the length of the rail, allowed some further scope in the decorations, mentioned earlier, (chapter three). As on the transoms, each builder used his favourite design. There are numerous varieties of scrollwork, some of which are illustrated.

Thoma II must have the most intricate of these decorations and, although built as a barge yacht, still has the Howard daffodils and particular type of lettering in her name.

Arthur White of Conyer used the style shown on the bow of *Joy*. *Persevere* is typical of all the Smeed-Dean barges, *Arcades* built as *Olive Mary* 1921, has the elaborate designs given to the barges from the Sittingbourne yard between 1920 and 1924. Some firms incorporated the house flag in the design on the badges. *Henry* is an example of this. The steel barges did not generally sport any badges, but Everard of Greenhithe reverted to the old practice as shown in the bow of *Will Everard*.

A heavy oak 'rigging' or 'channel' chock was fitted in way of the main rigging and acted as support for the rigging chain plates and also to keep the leeboards in position, the leeboard head iron passing through the channel cut through the chock at deck level.

Across the top of the transom was bolted the heavy saddle chock of similar height to the rails and 6 inches in thickness. Iron fairleads were fitted on the saddle chock and bow rail abaft the stem, and hawse pipes through the rail and bow badge chock. The anchor snatch or fairlead was bolted to the port side of the stem head.

The bigger the barge the higher the rails were built, very often with an extra board above the bow rail similar to that fitted aft on the quarter rails. These bow boards varied in length and depth. Some as much as 15 inches deep and reaching from the fore horse to stem, others from stem to the round of the bow of a uniform depth, and others the same length but tapering toward the aft end.

Inside the rails were fitted various cleats for use in mooring or to make fast running gear. The largest being the bow cleat fitted at the round of the bow, with others on the rigging chock and quarter rails.

On top of the bow rail in small or medium size barges is the socket for the rowing iron, the

49

24. *Rail decorations.*

Joy

Henry

Arcades

Persevere

Will Everard

25. *Rail decorations.*

rowlock of the barges. The heavy 25-30 foot sweeps, whose wielding was both heart and back breaking work, were often in use in the smaller barges working up through the London Bridges and were used with good effect in craft up to the 100 ton capacity, but in bigger craft, apart from helping the vessel's head around in light airs, very little use was made of them.

The arrangement on deck aft varied with the size of the barge, but generally a raised cambered cabin top was built about 12-15 inches above deck level, with access to the cabin through a sliding hatch and companion ladder on the port side, with a skylight either lifting off entirely when needed or having hinged flaps. The deeper hulled barges often had sufficient head room under the deck without the addition of the cabin top, but in these craft a large skylight about 3 feet by 2 ft. 6 ins. high stood over the centre of the cabin, glass sided, with wooden flap top

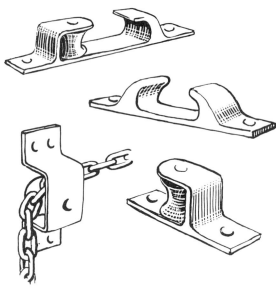

26. *Various types of iron fairlead, including that used for the anchor cable, bottom left.*

and the glass protected with iron or brass rods. A tell-tale compass could usually be found on gimbals inside the skylight. Entrance to the cabin was through a scuttle hatch, with small folding doors and a sliding top, situated most conveniently but always on the port side.

The flange and chimney from the cabin stove led through the forward part of the cabin top in craft so built, but in the flush decked barges, it was close to the skylight or scuttle.

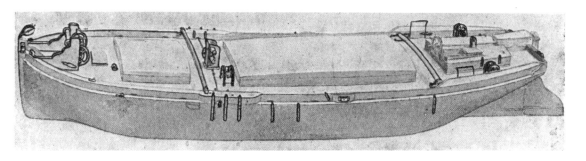

27. *General view pinpointing deck fittings.*

CHAPTER SIX

Blacksmith's work and fittings

THE blacksmith was a very important member of the yard, being concerned with all the ironwork incorporated in the hull and also with the fittings around the deck. A heavy stemband protects the face of the stem and forefoot, the top section terminating with a forged eye to take the bolt connecting the lower stayfall block to the stem head, and the whole bolted to the stem with heavy drift bolts up to 17 inches in length.

The heavy chain plates usually three in number but in some craft two only, were bolted through to the frames from outside the hull and had an eye at the top to which the lower dead eye was joined with shackle or forged link. Other plates of smaller dimensions were also fitted for main runners or vangs. The bowsprit barges had plates for the bowsprit shrouds either on the gunwale at the round of the bow or on the bow rail just above, with an extra eye for hooking on the rolling vangs, and also a snatch or roller fairlead fitted around the light water line on the stem for the chain bobstay.

The bitt on which the bowsprit heel pivoted

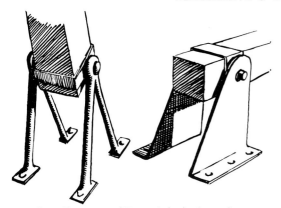

28. *Two types of Bowsprit heel tabernacle.*

had various patterns, from iron rod or plate structures forward of the windlass, to that found in some big coasters with the double windlass. This consisted of an oak post passing down through the deck and morticed into the keelson. It served a double purpose by carrying the heel

of the bowsprit and the centre pawls for the windlass which were fitted to its after side.

The tabernacle or mast box of the modern barges, generally referred to as the mast case, is a heavy iron structure which, with its base, weighs around 4 cwt. and is securely bolted to the deck and sailing beams below. Originally the mast box was constructed of wood with a small winch on the forward side to assist in heaving on the main brails. The winch on the modern mast case is geared, with two barrels on either side, and is the general purpose winch both for moving the barge and handling the running gear when extra power is needed. (Fig. 29). The iron strap, to which are connected the leeboard head irons, generally passes under the base of the mast box, but many barges have the iron plate attached to the base of the box. The lee-board head iron passes across the deck through the channel in the rigging chock, and supports

55

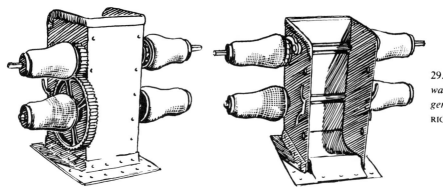

29. LEFT. *View from forward of Mast case with its general purpose gear winch.* RIGHT. *View from aft.*

the leeboard head. The main brail winch (Fig. 32), is bolted to the deck on the port side of the mast case and is usually a single purpose winch, but larger barges often have bigger winches containing drums for main brails, tops'l halyard and fores'l halyard, with an extra winch fitted

on the starboard side for the bowsprit jib stay.

The windlass, the most powerful part of the barge's equipment, is fitted to the heavy wood bitts that pass through the deck to the floor timbers, having large oak knees bracing the forward side on deck.

56

The core of the barrel is of iron with wood filling pieces making the whole an octagonal barrel, to the outside of which are spiked welts of oak and deal alternatively. At the ends of the barrel and, in the case of the double windlass, around the middle of the barrel as well, are the ruffles to engage the pawls. These pawls are fitted to the deck opposite the ends of the windlass, also to the centre bitt, if fitted. The double windlass was larger than the ordinary windlass with a much longer barrel, and had the port half of the barrel for the main anchor cable, and the starboard half for the second bower cable, or the bobstay when in use.

The gearing of the windlass made it possible for a man to heave the anchor up to the snatch single-handed under reasonable conditions even on the bigger barges. To hold the cable whilst fleeting (changing from one end of the barrel to the other) or for any reason which needs the barrel clear of cable, iron dogs or claws attached to the deck by a small length of chain, can be hooked on to the cable.

On the outside of the bitts are large cleats for mooring, and the tops of the bitts, frequently used for checking ropes, are often shaped to leave twin stubs around which to surge the check line. On the forward side and high up on the bitts, single barrel dolly winch is fitted. This is useful when heaving the barge around in dock or any other enclosed space. Before the cost of cotton rope became so exorbitant, a line of 1 inch in circumference and up to 50 fathoms in length was favoured for use on the dolly winch, but nowadays wire of $\frac{7}{8}$ inch circumference is more economical and makes a good substitute.

In the days when large stacks of hay and straw or timber were carried on deck, the main brails were led forward to the dolly, the working winches being buried under the deck load, but, unless a purchase was rigged, to heave the mainsail up, especially if full of wind, meant a heavy struggle. Another use for the dolly winch is now almost forgotten and belongs to the days when heaving out cargo with the barge's own tackle was a common event. A large gin wheel on a wire leg of about 4-6 feet was shackled to both tops'l sheet and halyard, these having been disconnected from their respective positions on the sail. A long runner, leading from the dolly winch fitted on the fore coaming, passed up through the gin wheel, down to deck level and was fitted with a hook or rope strop according to the cargo to be discharged. By adjusting sheet or halyard the gin could be plumbed over any part of the mainhold and all that was needed was two strong men to heave on the winch. When discharging the forehold the dolly would be returned to its normal position on the bitts and the gin suspended on the tops'l halyard only

58

30. TOP. *Normal side pawl windlass.* CENTRE. *Assembly of welts and ruffles to iron axle.* BOTTOM. *Centre pawl windlass usually to be found on the larger bowsprit barges.*

before the topmast. A guy rope from the leg of the gin wheel was used for finer positioning.

Just abaft the windlass is the forecastle hatch, usually a flat trap hatch with heavy cover, fastened down in bad weather by an iron bar hooked to an eye in the deck on one side, fitted down over the hatch and pegged down over another eye bolt on the opposite side. Some barges, generally the larger craft, had scuttle hatches. Howard of Maldon sometimes fitted a round hatch but this was unusual. The chain pipes leading to the cable lockers were usually close to the forecastle hatch and large iron bollards were generally fitted on deck near the round of the bow. Occasionally wooden bitts were fitted passing through the deck and fastened to the framework below.

The forehorse of oak, iron, or wire, was rigged just before the mast from the forward ends of the rigging chocks. Barges engaged in stack work

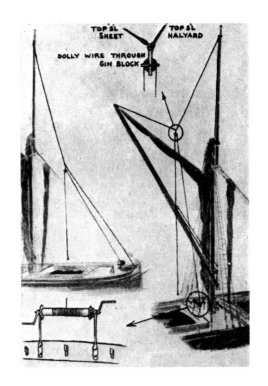

31.   *Dolly winch used in conjunction with topsail gear for handling cargo.*

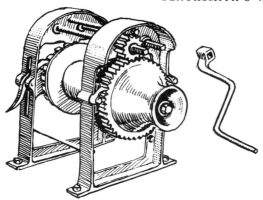

32. *Crab winch for raising and lowering leeboards. Note general purpose barrel for moorings and gear.*

These chocks were generally shaped with horns for making fast mooring ropes. The horse itself, of oak and averaging 6-8 inches in diameter and as much as 10 inches in big craft, was so shaped that when the sail was sheeted home amidships it would travel to either side without any attention. A heavy iron traveller with an eye to take the hook of the mainsheet block carried the sail across the horse.

Crab winches (Fig. 32), were fitted on either quarter and used in raising and lowering leeboards, with an independent barrel for heaving in moorings, vangs, mainsheets, etc. Occasionally upright capstan type winches were fitted, the lower half to work the leeboards, and the top half for general work.

Davits were fitted in most Estuary barges and the common practice was to have them shipped on the starboard quarter, so that when the boat was swung inboard in dock, it did not interfere

favoured the wire horse as being easier to remove and allowing of better stowage on deck, but the wooden or iron horse is in more general use.

The main horse was a permanent fitting bolted down on chocks abaft the main hatch.

33. *Stack barge's davit.*

Fig. 33. The barge being lightly laden, these davits would lift the boat high enough to keep her clear of the water when under way. When not in use the davits would stow away in any odd corner.

with entrance to the cabin. A very early type of davit in use on stack barges is illustrated in

CHAPTER SEVEN

Rudder and Lee-boards

THE rudder, of heavy construction, consisted of a heavy oak rudder post 12 inches square, with the fan made up of 9 inch strakes through bolted to the post, and the whole hinged to the stern post on heavy gudgeon irons, with a rudder bolt of $2\frac{1}{4}$-$2\frac{1}{2}$ inch diameter iron. The steering was, of course, originally a tiller arm but later chain or screw gear came in to general use. (Fig. 34). The chain gear is the simplest and easiest to repair in an emergency, consisting of chains from the short iron tiller arm passing through sheaves on the rail or

chocks, to a drum abaft the cabin top geared to the wheel spindle. The wheel, usually iron with wood handgrips, was at the forward end of the cabin top with a ratchet, or drum brake, just abaft it. Sometimes a wooden wheel with brass bands and centre cap was fitted, with the barge's name and port of registry on the rim and the builder's name on the centre cap.

The screw steering consists of an iron collar fitted on the head of the rudder post, to which are attached two arms of uneven length. These are connected to separate sleeves on the worming

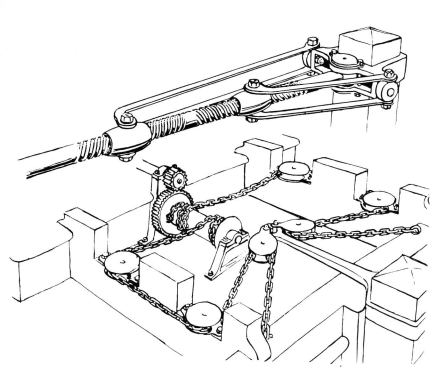

34. *Steering gear.*
ABOVE. *Screw.*
BELOW. *Chain.*

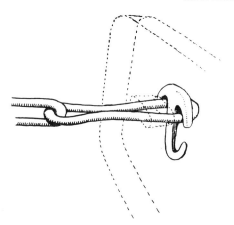

35. *The usual link and toggle arrangement.*

decked barges the position of the wheel can vary considerably and it is usually situated well aft: in the case of the mule rigged barge it is abaft the mizzen and skylight. Craft with a cabin top can fit a binnacle and stand to the deck in front of the wheel, but this is usually only shipped when required.

The lee-boards are made of oak planks 12-15 inches wide and up to 3 inches thick strapped together with iron bands and large iron plates on both sides of the head. The length varies according to the barge, the average is 16-18 feet, the widest part being at the aft end and generally equal to the depth of the barge's side or a little over. The bevelled leading edge rises to the head which is roughly one-third of the depth of the fan or aft end. Some variation in the shape of the leading edge and depth of the fan have appeared at times, usually in craft competing in the Sailing Matches. The lee-board is supported

of the spindle. The worming is cut in two opposite directions meeting in the centre, the effect being, when the spindle is turned, to push one arm and pull the other, and thereby moving the rudder to port or starboard. With flush-

by the head irons, rods connecting to the mastcase plate and passing across the deck with long links at the outboard end. The end link passes under the channel chock and through a slot in the head of the lee-board, and the operation is completed by fitting a toggle through the end of the link protruding through the lee-board head. Another variety of toggle is known as a mushroom fitting. A two and a half inch iron bolt with mushroom shaped head is passed through a round hole in the lee-board head and shackled to the lee-board head irons. A short preventer chain is fitted from the top edge of the lee-board head to the most convenient chain plate. The raising and lowering of the lee-boards is by means of a pendant, generally of $\frac{3}{8}$ to $\frac{1}{2}$ inch chain shackled halfway down the fan, passing through a snatch block fitted to the rail and leading aft. It terminates in a single-sheave iron block through which is rove the

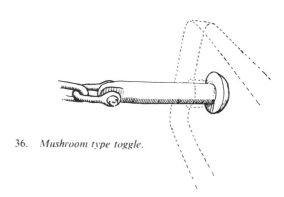

36. *Mushroom type toggle.*

wire or chain fall whose standing end is fastened well aft near the main horse chock, the running end leading to the main barrel of the crab-winch on the quarter. Early barges used a rope purchase in place of the wire fall and had no quarter winches. The one hundred ton barge *Bassildon* was so rigged until early in the 1940's.

65

CHAPTER EIGHT

Accommodation and other details

THE cabin was generally occupied by both members of the barge's crew, although in many larger craft the mate and third hand, if carried, lived in the forecastle. The cabin was entered by a ladder in the companion way and had a door hinged to fold either wholly or in two halves back to the port side. In some barges the door was made of solid mahogany, and sometimes fitted with glass panels protected by brass rods in the top half of the door. The panelwork in the cabin was often of natural mahogany, pitch pine, or pitch pine and birds-eye maple and brightly varnished. When a natural finish was not used, graining and varnishing was preferred to plain painting. Drawers and cupboards were fitted in the panel work. The aft-end cupboard space was always referred to by barge-men as the 'Yarmouth Roads', but what the connection is with this famous road-stead one can only guess. The most logical suggestion seems to be that both are usually wet. The steering gear is directly over this cupboard space and the terrific strain this gear gets at times would account for the fact that it

37. *A cosy retreat. The barge's cabin.*

is the most difficult place to keep free from leaks. The sleeping accommodation consists of built-in bunks, the skipper to starboard, the mate to port. In some barges a small 'state-room' was built on the skipper's side, but more usually sliding doors or curtains were fitted in the entrance to the bunks. The table was hinged to the aft panelling or to the transom locker and was supported from the cabin beams or by a leg to the floor. Occasionally in the larger barges a four-legged table would be fitted. Built-in lockers running round the two sides of the aft end of the cabin were useful as seats and as storage space for coal and wood for the fire. A fireplace, generally an open stove but sometimes a range, was fitted at the forward end of the cabin. Lighting was by paraffin lamp either mounted in gymbals or swinging from the cabin beams.

The cabin was usually a snug retreat, although a lot depended upon the crew, but with the polished panelling and brasswork and a cheery fire it had an air of solid comfort. With the installation of engines the cabin is used as an engine room, and the crew move forward to the forecastle. Originally the forecastle was the general store-room of the barge, or in most craft the fittings consisted of a cable locker, racks for sails and rope and lamp and paint cupboards. In the bigger barges, where the crew lived forward, there was a different layout consisting of fold-back cots for the crew with lockers and cupboards, and a cooking range.

Wheelhouses were very rare in sailing barges and only found on a few of the coasters, but with the installation of auxiliary power a wheelhouse has been added to the usual deck fittings.

The light screens were fitted on iron legs standing in sockets on the rigging chocks (Fig.

38). The screens were made to unship when going alongside. The stern light was fitted on the saddle chock.

Other useful items in a barge's equipment were the 'setting-booms', long poles 25-30 feet in length with an iron spike and wooden shoe at the lower end and shaped at the top end to rest against the shoulder of the user. These were used when 'poking up' some narrow creek too narrow to allow the barge to sail with a foul wind. 'Setting-booms', with the sweeps mentioned earlier, and boat hooks, usually referred to as 'hitchers' were stowed on the main hatchway when not in use. They were kept in place by spar battens, sometimes made of 4 by 1 inch timber slightly less than the width of the hatchway, with chocks at either end, or of short end chocks connected by suitable lengths of rope.

The ground tackle varied in size with the barge, the main bower anchor varying from two

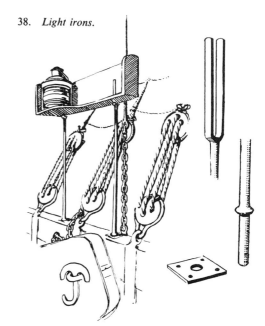

38. *Light irons.*

and a half cwt. in small barges to about four cwt. in coasters. The cable was from five-eights inch in the smallest barges to one inch in the largest, the average being seven-eights inch black iron cable. A spare or second bower with a collapsible stock was stowed on deck together with a kedge of about 1 cwt. Some barges working in creeks had a small single fluke anchor, which was taken ashore and hooked in the saltings to heave themselves around. A minimum of 45 fathoms of cable in 15 fathoms lengths (in coasters 60 fathoms) was shackled to the main bower, and spare cable up to 60 fathoms was carried in the cable locker for use with the second bower. The handy line or horse line of at least 50 fathoms of three to three and a half inch manila, tow ropes of 15 fathoms of 6–7 inch grass and mooring ropes of 5-6 inch grass or manila made up the equipment, although most barge-men carried more than the amount specified to allow for emergencies.

The dinghy, elm planked and oak framed, averaged 12–15 feet in length and was generally beamy and shallow. There were three thwarts, the section forward of the head thwart being boarded in and known as the head sheets, and benches fitted from the aft thwart and to the stern. Thole pins of oak were favoured for rowing but the favourite form of propulsion was known to bargemen as sculling—not to be confused with the usual application of this term. The bargeman stands in the stern of the dinghy and uses a single oar. The oar rests in the sculling hole in the top of the transom and is moved so that the blade describes a 'figure of eight' in the water. The pressure of the oar against the transom provides the forward thrust.

CHAPTER NINE

PART **3**

Masts and Rigging

THE mainmast of pitchpine, with its ironwork, is the heaviest of a barge's spars and it is a rare occurrence for a barge to be completely dismasted through breaking this spar, although carrying away a topmast is not so uncommon. Sprits, too, are sometimes broken but mainly through heavy jerking as the barge rolls, or a heavy gybe.

Mast sizes vary with the size and tonnage of the barge, the average for the 120-ton hull would be about 30 ft. under hounds to heel with 5 to 6 ft. head or doubling, and 10–12 inches diameter above the squared heel, tapering slightly towards the hounds. The heel is square in section to fit the mast box, and shod with an iron plate under the rounded heel to take the friction imposed when lowering and raising the mast.

The jackstay (Fig. 39 K), fitted aft of the spar, is of $\frac{3}{4}$ in. diameter iron rod, passing through eye bolts driven in the mast, carries the luff of the mainsail.

Other fittings illustrated in Fig. 39 are the topmast cap (A), fitted and bolted to the mast head. The two small blocks are for the crosstree

71

topping lifts. (B) Iron band with lugs to carry the bowsprit jib halyards and jib stay. (C) Iron plate bolted through the masthead, having a lug on which seats the eye of the fore stay, and an eye to take the yard tackle purchase. (D) and (DD), Iron trestle trees, bolsters to carry hounds of stanliff and main shrouds, and the lower topmast cap. (E) Crosstree beds bolted to the trestle trees forward of the mast. Note lugs for foresail halyards at each side of lower cap under beds. (F) Cross trees hinged on the bed plate, the arms rest between lugs at either end of the beds. The arms are hinged to allow them to be raised close alongside the mast head when coming or lying alongside other craft or high obstructions which would otherwise foul the backstays passing through the crutch at the extreme ends of the arm. The stays were secured against falling out by passing a pin across the ends of the crutch. The second crutch, inboard

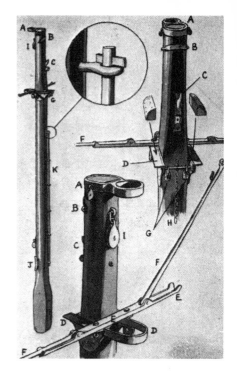

39. *Mainmast.* LEFT. *The entire spar from portside.* BOTTOM CENTRE. *The 'Doubling' from starboard forward.* TOP RIGHT. *Doubling from aft.*

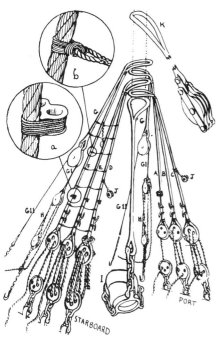

40. *Mainmast standing rigging, note dressing order beginning with Stanliff.*

of the end, was for the use of a second standing backstay if rigged. (G) Iron bar carrying two iron blocks through which are rove the main peak brails. (H) Preventer chain connected to nock of mainsail. (I) Iron block to carry topmast heel rope. (J) Cleat for topsail halyard and lug and block for topsail halyard fall, but the latter was not a general fitting as the majority of barges had the topsail halyard lower block shackled on the muzzle fitting of the sprit.

The procedure for dressing the main mast is shown in Fig. 40. The shrouds and the stanliff which supports the heel of the sprit, are of 3 in. galvanised iron wire, the shrouds being set up with 3 in. tarred hemp lanyards rove through dead eyes 6 in. in diameter. The eye of the 4 in. iron wire forestay (K) fits over the mast head, and rests on the lug aft of the mast head. Fig. 39 (C). The lower end of the forestay is shackled to the upper block of the stayfall tackle, the

73

latter comprising two 3-sheave iron blocks and a fall of $2\frac{1}{4}$ inch galvanised wire 25 fathoms in length. The lower block of this purchase is bolted to the eye at the top of the stem band. The method of reeving shroud lanyards is shown in Fig. 40, commencing at port (A) and the final stage shown at starboard (D). Iron cleats are seized on above the dead eyes, and above the cleats, the fairleads for peak brails, and clewline (inset a). The bullseye fairleads (J) on the fore shrouds are for staysail sheets.

Ratlines of $1\frac{1}{4}$ to $1\frac{1}{2}$ inch tarred hemp are seized and hitched to the starboard shrouds from dead eyes to close under the hounds, clove hitched round the middle shroud and the eye at each end of the ratline seized with marline as in inset (b).

The main runners (g) are hooked into chain plates abaft the shrouds and set up with the rope purchase (h), the fall leading through leg (gl)

74

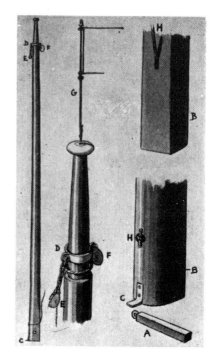

41. *Topmast.* LEFT. *Entire spar from port side.* CENTRE. *Pole, showing assembly of hounds band and grommet. Also 'Bob' frame and spindle, withdrawn to show barbed point.* TOP RIGHT. *Heel from starboard aft.* BOTTOM RIGHT. *Heel from port forward, also iron 'fid'.*

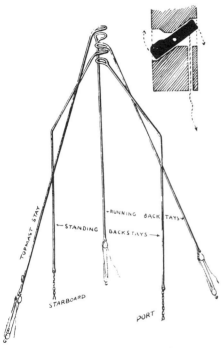

42. *Topmast standing rigging, showing order of dressing. See also inset of topmast patent tripping. 'Fid'.*

and made fast with rolling hitch on leg (gII).

The topmast (Fig. 41) of Norwegian Fir, is roughly the same length from truck to heel as the overall length of the mainmast, 8–9 ins. diameter at the heel tapering to around 7 inches at the hounds. The pole (above the hounds) varies in length from 3–4 ft. and is surmounted by the bob, as the barge's flag is known.

The 'bob', flown at the topmast head, is the 'house flag' of the owner and illustrations of the present day owners' colours can be found at the end of this book.

The topmast is rigged to lower through the caps at the mainmast head when it is necessary to lower the gear to the deck.

When rigged aloft it rests on a fid (A) passing through the hole in the heel of the spar (B), the ends of the fid resting on the lower cap of the main trestle trees. A wire heel rope (H), fitted through the topmast heel, leads through the

75

block (I) on the mainmast head. A rope tackle or, alternatively, a single block with chain fall leading to the mast case winch, connected with the heel rope, and supplied the purchase to raise and lower the topmast. To house the topmast weight is taken on the heel rope, the fid removed, the fall slackened away and the top-mast lowered until the hounds are just above the main mast head.

Another form of fid used in river barges is illustrated in inset on Fig. 42, and is designed to pivot and rest inside the topmast heel when the weight is taken off, and pulled into the square position with a tripping line leading to the deck. This type of fid operates from the deck, and saves the climb aloft to put the fid in when rigging out.

Fittings illustrated in Fig. 41 are: (C) iron toe fitted in front of heel to prevent topmast being hove up clear of the lower cap, (D) topmast head band carrying the staysail halyard block

(E) and topsail halyard block (F). The band is fitted to a shoulder cut in the topmast at hound level and is seated on a tarred hemp grommet. (G) 'Bob' frame and spindle, the latter driven in to the topmast pole.

When rigged the topmast is supported by a minimum of five stays and dressed in the order shown in Fig. 42, commencing with the port standing backstay (as the bargemen describe the stay passing through the crosstree end to the tackle at the rigging chock) and finishing with the stem or short topmast stay, and, in barges with bowsprits, with the long topmast stay to the bowsprit end fitted after the stem stay. The running backstays and short topmast stay are set up with tackles to stem head and rails.

When the topmast is rigged the heel rope fall is disconnected and stowed away and the heel rope stowed down the stanliff and stopped off on the stanliff links.

CHAPTER TEN

Sprit, Mainsail and Topsail

THE sprit lengths vary slightly even in barges of similar tonnage, depending on the shape of the mainsail, whether high peaked or square, but the average for 100-ton barges is around 50 ft. O.A., 54–56 ft. in 140–160 ton craft with a maximum of 65 ft. in the *Will Everard*. The four 'Everards' had the biggest sail plan of all spritsail barges, measuring 112 ft. from deck to topmast truck, sprits of 65 ft. and working sail area of five and a half thousand square feet of canvas. One unusual feature of the *Will Everard* are the ratlines fitted above the main hounds to allow the crew to reach the mainmast head with its 'doubling' of 14 feet as opposed to the average 5–6 ft.

Sprits were mainly of Oregon or Pitch pine, usually Oregon, but steel sprits were to be seen during the 30's in the Mistley and Ipswich barges.

Pitch pine spars were smaller in diameter than Oregon, the latter averaging 10–11 inches at the heel, 12–14 inches in the middle and 9–10 inches at the joggle or outer end.

An iron band is fitted midway along the spar,

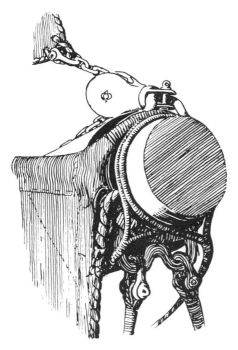

43. *Sprit head dressing. 1st Iron band for topsail sheet and vangs. 2nd Eye of mainsail head rope. 3rd Rolling vangs.*

to which is attached the yard tackle (Fig. 50(a)). A. the wire leading through a block fitted to the lug at back of the mainmast head (Fig. 39(c)) down the mast, and generally fitted with a tackle. Sometimes a chain tail was employed being set up on the mast case winch if needed, or made fast at the heel of the mainmast.

The vangs to control the sprit are of 2–2½ inch wire, shackled usually to short chain legs from the sprit end band, and leading to a rope purchase at the lower end. Extra vangs are fitted usually with eyes to fit over the sprit end to assist in keeping the sprit under control when the barge is rolling. When not in use these 'rolling' vangs are loosely twisted round the sprit,—or, if on the short side, led straight down and hitched to the links of the muzzle. (Fig. 50). To rig, the rolling vangs are taken outside all backstays and shrouds and connected to a tackle leading to the bow. The lee vang is then set up, pinning

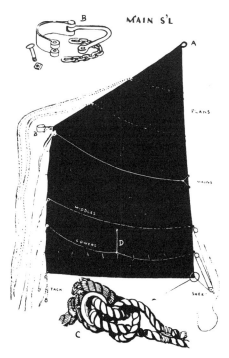

MAIN S'L

B

A

PEAKS

MAINS

MIDDLES

LOWERS

D

TACK

SHEET

C

44. *Mainsail showing lead of Brails, sheet and tack.*

the sprit between the main vang to weather and the rolling vang to lee. When at sea rolling vangs were led through a large ring fairlead suspended on the standing backstays, to keep the tackles, etc., out of the lee-board head and getting cut or otherwise getting foul.

The downward thrust of the sprit when rigged is taken by the stanliff, and the spar is held close to the mast by the muzzle and band (Fig. 40(I)). Adjustment to the stanliff length is made by taking up, or adding to, the chain links at the lower end, either when the gear is lowered on deck, or by raising the heel with tackles when the spars are erect. The outer end of the sprit fits in the large eye of the mainsail headrope.

The mainsail is bent on with the spars lowered on deck. The sail is folded to a long sausage with the eye (A) at one end and the tack at the other, but so folded that the luff and leech ropes are clear. The eye (A) is dragged aft and fitted over the sprit end and the collar band (B) fitted around the mast and passed through the nock thimble. Occasionally a wire lashing is used and, although a finer adjustment can be made to the position of the throat of the mainsail in this way, the iron collar fittings illustrated are easier and quicker to handle.

The luff of the mainsail is attached to the jackstay by graduated shackles. A few barges had a chain jackstay shackled to the collar, passing through eye bolts at the after side of the mast and fastened to the heel of the spar. The luff was seized on to loose thimbles on this jackstay with spun yarn robands.

The main brails, of wire, lead both sides of the sail from a light chain or tarred hemp strop worked through cringles in the leach of the sail, through iron blocks attached to the nock, and shackled to a single wire leg led to the winch on deck to port of the mainmast.

80

45. *Mainsheet block and traveller showing method of belaying sheet on extended pin.*

The peak brails are spliced or seized to the leach and lead each side of the sail through blocks seized to the headrope, then through the blocks at mast hounds. (Fig. 39(g)), down the line of the aft main shrouds through spectacles (Fig. 40(a)) and are made fast as required to the cleats on the shrouds.

The lower and middle brails are of rope rove round the sail, knotted clear of the blocks at the luff and leading to the deck, being made fast as required to cleats on the mast box. The 'lowers' pass through 'stirrups' to prevent fouling the foot of the sail.

The main tack purchase illustrated comprises a chain shackled to a cringle in the luff, passing through a block at the base of the mast, back through the tack cringle and set up with a rope purchase shackled to a ring in the deck, but variations on this fitting are innumerable. The mainsheet, of 3 inch manila, is hitched to the

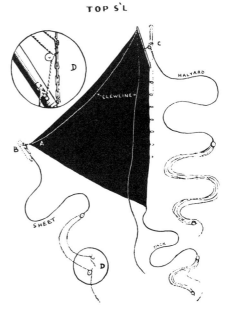

TOP S'L

46. Topsail. Inset shows sheet lead to stanliff and sprit heel.

clew of the sail with a fisherman's bend as illustrated, or eye-spliced and shackled. From the sheet cringle it passes through the main sheet block, port side, bottom to top, up to the lower single block on the leech of the sail, passing through this block from top to bottom, then down to the starboard side of the main block, passing through from bottom to top, back to the upper single block on the leech, passing through from bottom to top, and down to make fast, as illustrated (Fig. 45) on pin. The main-sheet block hooks into the iron traveller on the mainhorse and should be 'moused' across the hook.

The topsail can be bent whilst the gear is on deck and, to an experienced crew, is a simple operation, but the simplest and clearest way is to wait until the spars are erect and then bend on as follows. Fold the sausage shape with head-stick eyelets at one end and tack at the other.

The headstick is lashed on with wire seizings at ends of stick and spunyarn robands at intervals along the spar. The clewline block is then attached to the top end of the headstick, the clewline spliced into the clew (Fig. 46(a)) and led through the block and left loose until bending is completed. The sail is stopped up at intervals of about 3 ft. and the head is hove to mainmast head level on the staysail halyards, the standing part of the topsail halyard is then shackled on to the head stick band, and, the staysail halyard having been removed, the sail hauled up in the usual manner.

The topmast hoops are bent on with spunyarn seizings by a crew member seated on the main-mast head as the sail is hauled up. The sheet pendant is shackled on to the clew, the tack pendant attached, and the clewline led through the fairlead block in the main rigging to bullseye and cleat on the starboard middle shroud. The

47. *Topsail clewed home.*

48. *Topsail seen from truck height.*
   Note lead of clewline.

stops are then cut from the sail as the halyards are slackened down. The sail is then set in the usual manner of hauling out the sheet as far as possible, hoisting the head as high as possible, then setting up sheet and tack. The tack purchase can lead from an eyebolt on the lower end of the sprit or from the deck, the fall being made fast on the sprit in the former position, and a cleat on the mast box in the latter. To stow the topsail the head is allowed to run down and the slack of the clewline is taken up, the sheet let go and the sail clewed in snug to the hounds as in Fig. 47. This operation is easy to carry out with the wind ahead or on the port side but, whilst it can be overcome with conditions otherwise, it may be very difficult. With the sail clewed home, a gasket fast at the mainmast head is passed round the head of the sail, and another gasket from the main hounds passed around the lower part of the sail. Fig. 48 gives a sea-gull view of the topsail set. A second clewline is sometimes rigged and is made fast at the headstick end, leading down the port side of the sail through a fairlead block on the stanliff below the hounds and down to the middle starboard shroud cleat. The use of this second clewline makes the task of stowing a topsail in a breeze easier, as the sail is held close in to the main rigging by the two clewlines and cannot balloon out as so often happens when head to wind.

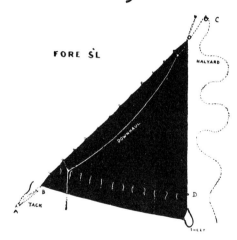

CHAPTER ELEVEN

Topsail, Mizzen and Layout

THE foresail (Fig. 49) is folded and stopped up to leave the luff rope clear, it is then seized on to the hanks on the forestay starting from the top hank, and hauling up on the halyard as each hank is seized on. The stops are cut and the sheet, usually of chain, is shackled on to the two clew cringles, and the down haul spliced on to the halyard cringle and rove down to port through fairleads at top and lower hanks. The tack purchase illustrated is a common form in use, but in some cases a single part is used and lashed down before the halyards are set up, but

49. *Fore s'l, showing permanent sheet and bowline cringle.*

this is only practised in the smaller barges. The lower block (A) is attached to the stem head and the upper block (B) is hooked into the tack cringle when the sail is set and easily removable when stowing away. The halyards are shackled to the lug under the starboard side of the crosstree beds, led through the single block at the head of the sail, up to the single block (C) under the port side of the crosstree beds and finally to the cleat on the forward port shroud.

To stow the sail the halyards are let go, the downhaul hauled down tight, tack unhooked, the sail rolled inwards from foot and leech to make a neat roll and the downhaul used as a furling line passed right-handed round the sail and pulled tight at each turn.

The bowline, used to 'back' the sail when winding, is usually a one-time shroud lanyard, and one is spliced to each forward shroud. When needed the end of the bowline is passed through

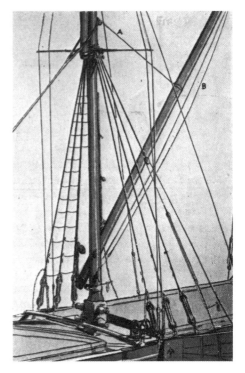

50. *Standing rigging only.*

cringle (D), back round outside fore and middle shrouds, pulled tight and made fast on the cleat on middle shroud.

Fig. 50 gives the general layout and view of the standing rigging only, around the mainmast; Fig. 51 the running rigging only, with stowed main and foresail. The tackle (A) is the burton purchase generally fitted in barges with no davits and used in conjunction with the vangs or runner falls to raise the dinghy to the hatchway.

As mentioned earlier there are two types of mizzen rig in use. On the one hand the more usual 'steering' sail of the river, and on the other the larger gaff and boom sail as carried by *Will Everard* and *Cambria*, the last of the mule-rigged coasters.

Fig. 52 shows the general layout of spars and fittings of the steering sail, insert (A) gives the details of the mast head band with two lugs, one for forestay and one for the mizzen throat

87

51. *Running rigging only.*

shackle. Inset (B) illustrates the make-up of the boom goose-neck fitting.

Other items are:—

(C) jackstay;

(D) cleats for brail and sheet;

(Di) „ „ „

(E) wedge on boom to position strop or band to which is shackled sheet purchase;

(F) lug at boom end, to which is shackled the clew of the sail.

The mast is held in the small tabernacle by a bolt passing through the heel and the case. The bolt acts as a pivot when the mast is being lowered and, whilst some masts can be lowered both ways if need be, they are usually lowered or 'stooped' aft.

The dressing of the mast is illustrated in Fig. 40, the forestay shackled to the mast head

band, and the stanliff and two sets of shrouds are then put on over the masthead. Each pair of shrouds is made up from one wire seized at the hounds, inset (A).

The mast is hove up with the aid of a purchase rigged to the forestay, and the shrouds set up with tarred hemp lanyards. Inset (B) shows the muzzle and rings for supporting the heel of the sprit.

To bend the mizzen the sail is shackled by the throat to the mast band, shackled or seized to the jackstay, and the tack lashing made fast to the lug (Fig. 52), and the brails and topping lift rove off (Fig. 54). The sail is shackled to the boom end and the goose-neck shipped at the heel of the mast. The topping lift is spliced in to the shackle at the boom end and the sheet purchase between boom and rudder blade rove off. The sprit end is inserted in the eye of the headrope and the heel of the spar placed in the ring (C)

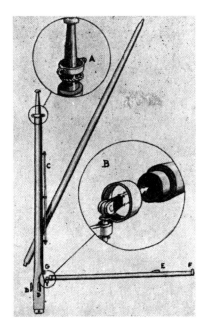

52. *Mizzen mast sprit and boom show-*
ing, inset, assembly of grommet and
hounds band, and boom gooseneck.

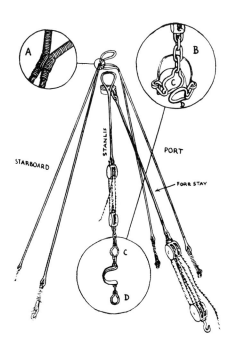

53. *Mizzen standing rigging.*

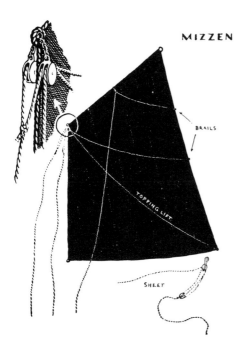

MIZZEN

BRAILS

TOPPING LIFT

SHEET

54. *Mizzen. Note inset, use of double block for topping lift and port brail leg.*

55. *General view from port quarter under way, but the mainsail brailed.*

with the stanliff fall overhauled. The tackle is then taken up and the heel pulled in to the mast, the muzzle put round the mast and the ring (D) slipped on the sprit end. When the sprit is set up in position, the stanliff fall is passed round the heel and made fast by a rolling hitch round its own parts and the rail of the fall tied up out of the way. To set the sail, all brails and the topping lift are let go and the sail sheeted down to the rudder. To stow, the sheet is let go, brails set up, topping lift pulled up and the peak brail is then taken up. The peak brail may be used as a vang to keep the sprit quiet when the sail is stowed by leading along the quarter deck to a cleat, or making fast at the main horse chock.

The mule mizzen is a heavier and bigger rig and survives from the ketch rig. The pitch pine mast of 35–40 ft. in length is stepped in a box just abaft the mainhorse and lowers forward only. Two shrouds on each side lead to chain plates and are set up with lanyards and deadeyes. The shrouds are spread to give support from forward and aft as well as sideways and no forestay is carried. A jump stay is fitted to support the masthead against the strain of the peak halyards. The sail is bent to a gaff and is generally retained aloft and stowed with brails. The clew of the sail is hauled out to the boom end when the sail is set by means of an outhaul and purchase. Two light vangs control the gaff end when the sail is stowed. An illustration of this mule mizzen appears in Fig. 11.

CHAPTER TWELVE

Handling and Maintenance

A LIGHT staysail is carried hanked to the stem stay (Fig. 56A), primarily for use in light winds but, depending on the size of the sail and strength of spar and stays, would often be held on to rather over long to gain a turn for discharge or loading, or to save a tide. The extra speed through the water going to windward was often, especially in narrow waters, outweighed by the amount of lee helm generally required after each tack, so, unless on a long leg or with a fair wind, carrying the staysail in a breeze was hardly worth the strain on the spar.

A good rule with sailing barges in short turning is to use the foresail alone as headsail if there is wind enough to draw the sail to leeward, or if not to stow the foresail and use the staysail. The staysail halyard leads down from the block E (Fig. 41) at the topmast head to the cleat on the forward starboard shrouds, the sheets rove through the fairleads on the forward shrouds (Fig. 40J), to cleats on shrouds or rigging chock, the latter position giving best results as the shrouds when to leeward give so much slack.

The staysail can be used as a 'spinnaker' (Fig.

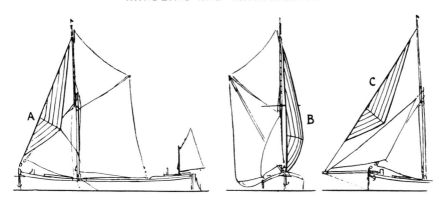

56. *Three ways of setting the standard light staysail.*

56B) when running before the wind by unhooking the stem stay complete with sail, and hooking on to a convenient position near the heel of the mainmast, the sheet being passed outside the standing backstay and all rigging and led aft to the mainhorse chock. In bow sprit

barges the staysails can be set over the bowsprit jib as a 'flying jib' (Fig. 56C) either bent on to the long topmast stay or as a temporary sail by reeving the dolly wire through the 'spare' sheave of the fiddle block at the bowsprit end, and shackled on to the stem stay. Then stay and

93

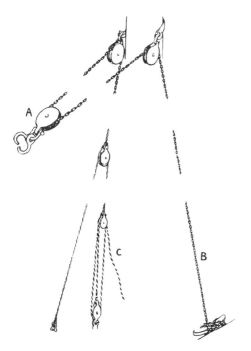

57. *Jib halyard and its purchases.*

sail are hove out together on the dolly winch.

Bowsprits are fitted to barges trading outside the river and on the coast. The spars vary in length to suit the sail plan of the barge, with an average length of 25 ft. in 120–150 ton barges. The bowsprit is of pitch pine or Oregon pine squared at the heel for about 4 feet, with a spider band at the outer end to carry shrouds, bobstay and stay block.

Fig. 58: Traveller (A); Outhaul (C); Inhaul (D); Bobstay (E); Long topmast stay (F); Shrouds (G); Gammon iron (H).

Racing craft often fitted special spars for the event and a bowsprit often had as much as 30 feet extending beyond the stem head. There are two ways of setting the jib, either on a stay or flying, i.e. hooking the tack on to the traveller and hauling out to the bowsprit end and then hooking the head to the chain halyard block (Fig. 58A) and setting up on the fall, (B) finally

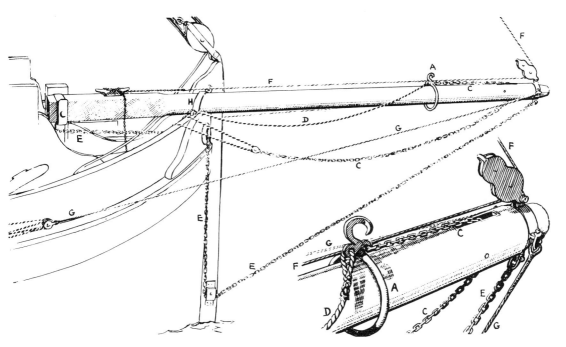

58.   *Bowsprit and its gear. Note lead of Bobstay to the windlass.*

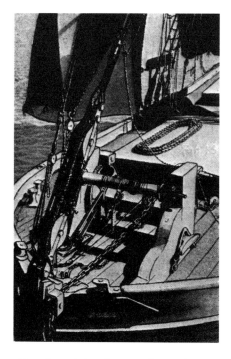

59. *General view from port bow underway.*

getting the luff taut by sweating up the purchase (C).

The big barges trading regularly on the coast favoured the stay-jib carried permanently on the spar, the stay set up on a winch to starboard of the mainmast and the sail set with rope halyards.

When not in use the bowsprit could be steeved up so that the spar and all its gear came abaft the line of the stem.

The barge's spars, as mentioned earlier, are designed to lower and raise. The stayfall and blocks used in lowering the gear are illustrated in Fig. 59. The rope stopper securing the fall can also be seen.

To lower the main gear, the topmast is housed, as explained earlier, the stayfall rove round the windlass drum for three turns, weight taken on the fall by heaving on the windlass and the stopper removed. The stayfall is surged round

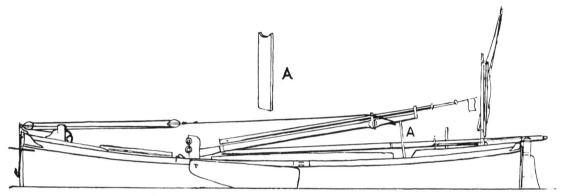

60. *Spars lowered. Note topmast struck and sprit resting on starboard taffrail.*

the windlass barrel and the spars lowered aft, until the mast finally rests on the mast prop standing on deck between mainhorse and coaming (Fig. 60A). Care should be taken when lowering the gear to see that the sprit is lowered to starboard of the wheel and mizzen gear.

To raise the rigging the stayfall is rode on the windlass barrel by dipping the end through several turns on the barrel and setting tight or, with several clear turns of fall on, stopped off on a staple at the end of the barrel.

When the gear is hove up into sailing position

97

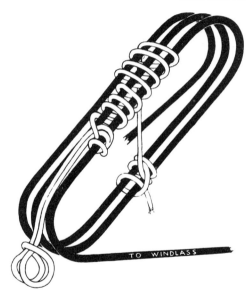

61. Diagram showing application of stay-fall stopper. Note the splice of the long eye is absorbed in first rolling hitch.

the stopper is put on as follows (Fig. 61). It is begun as in a rolling hitch, left-handed, but instead of making the final half hitch, it is turned back right-handed round two parts of the stayfall for four turns, then round all three turns of the fall four times, led down and neatly rolling hitched to the port and centre lower parts. As shown in the illustration the two parts of the long eye of the stopper extend into the first rolling hitch. The stayfall can then be taken off the windlass and stowed below deck. 'Bulldog' grips are often used as a safety measure in case the stopper is cut in any way, but care must be taken not to damage the wire of the fall or the serving. The stayfall is served for about 5 fathoms to protect the part permanently exposed from the weather.

Another item on Fig. 59 is the dolly winch fitted forward of the bitt heads, with its $\frac{7}{8}$ inch wire runner and a 2 inch rope tail.

The sails in a commercial barge needed dressing annually, the sails being unbent and spread out on shore, the bolt ropes given a coat of stockholm tar, and a mixture of linseed and cod oil, red and yellow ochre and water applied to both sides of the sails, allowing one side to dry before attempting the other.

Yacht barge sails, not having such heavy continuous wear, should only need dressing every two or even three years, except possibly in way of the main and peak brails where chafe takes place.

Spars and running rigging need checking over annually, blocks cleaned, oiled and painted, rope gear overhauled and wire gear thoroughly examined. Unless wire is new or still retaining grease in the heart, it should be wirebrushed and treated with a dressing of boiled linseed oil and white lead. Shroud lanyards should be removed and dressed with stockholm tar.

The mainmast should be well varnished but, if weathered, should be scraped and sandpapered and raw linseed oil applied. When dry give the spar a coating of linseed and varnish mixed, finishing off with two coats of varnish. If the spar is then washed off annually and varnished it should not need scraping again for 4 or 5 years. The same treatment can be given to the main sprit and all mizzen spars and bowsprit, but generally the sprit and often the mizzen spars are painted.

The 'working' part of the topmast (between hounds and cap) needs scraping annually in commercial craft but, unless the yacht barge owner wants to be really smart, the spar could be scrubbed off and scraped alternate years. When scraped the working part of the spar needs two coats of raw linseed and should not be varnished as the topsail hoops bind if varnish is used. The part of the topmast between the mast caps is treated the same as the mainmast, and the heel itself painted white for about one foot. The pole can be scraped and varnished or painted, the latter treatment being more usual.

The hull needs scrubbing and scraping up to the water line at least once a year and more often if lying still for any length of time, and a coat of tar up to deck level at least once each year. If, after a few years, the tar gets too thick on the sides, breaming, i.e. burning off, is necessary and improves the look of the hull. Heat is applied to the sides with a large blow lamp, care being taken not to fire the tar. As soon as the tar is running, scrape off the surplus. A fresh coat of tar should be applied after breaming. To assist in keeping the hull clean, plumbago (blacklead) mixed with water can be applied to the sides from wale to chines whilst the tar is tacky, and left until dry and then lightly rubbed down with a soft brush. Whilst not

claimed to be anti-fouling, it does retard the growth of weed and certainly makes scrubbing off much easier.

To clean off the actual bottom of a barge it is necessary to berth on a grid at some convenient yard. A garden hoe makes an efficient scraper under the bottom, keeping the person using the scraper clear of falling barnacles and weed, etc. The barge will need to move on the grid to allow all the bottom to be cleaned off. A barge needs scraping underneath usually every other year depending on the amount of time afloat and also the waters in which she lies.

With regard to the woodwork on deck, painting should be carried out at least once a year and the decks given two dressings of a good lead paint. Colours are a matter of personal taste but barges do not lend themselves to any gaudy colour scheme. Whilst some commercial firms had their own special colouring, the

100

'traditional' colours are as follows·—

Wooden blocks and any painted spars—*mast colour.*

Iron blocks and iron work on spars—*white or galvanised paint.*

Main and top mast hounds—*white.*

Iron work on deck (winches, etc)—*mid-green.*

Inside rails, hatch, coamings, horses, bitt-heads—*teak colour.*

Cabin top—*teak colour, with black edging to top.*

Quarter boards (and bow rail and capping if fitted)—*white.*

Rails—*black with primrose yellow streak and name.*

Bow and quarter badges—*green with primrose scrolls.*

Gunwales—*white.*

Decks—*light grey.*

Transom, if little decorated—*a green field with primrose lettering and white tuck, but, if with plenty of scrollwork, a black field.*

Rudder post *to match transom main colour.*

62. *The usual stages of sail reduction on the increase of wind force.*

RIGGING

Average lengths required for 100-130 ton barges.

1″ sisal or manila	2 crosstree topping lifts	- -	6 fathoms each
	2 ,, downhauls	- - -	4½ ,, ,,
1¼″	1 mizzen peak brail	- - -	7 ,, ,,
1½″	1 fore tack	- - - - - -	2 ,, ,,
	1 main tack fall	- - - - - -	1½ ,, ,,
	1 topsail	- - - - - -	3 ,, ,,
	1 mizzen topping lift	- - -	4 ,, ,,
	1 staysail tack line	- - - -	1 ,, ,,
	1 mizzen tack line	- - - -	2 ,, ,,
1¾″	4 main peak brails	- - - -	12½ ,, ,,
	1 2nd topsail clew line	- - -	12 ,, ,,
2″	1 staysail halyard	- - - -	22 ,, ,,
	1 foresail ,,	- - - - -	15 ,, ,,
	1 topsail ,,	- - - - -	20-25 according to number of sheaves in fall.
	1 foresail downhaul	- - -	6½ fathoms each
	1 topsail clewline	- - - -	18 ,, ,,
	1 mizzen stanliff fall	- - - -	5½ ,, ,,
	1 ,, brail	- - - - -	4½ ,, ,,
	1 ,, sheet	- - - - -	12 ,, ,,
	1 lower main brail	- - - -	14 ,, ,,
	1 middle ,, ,,	- - - -	14 ,, ,,
	1 topsail gasket (head)	- - -	2 ,, ,,
	1 topsail ,, (foot)	- - -	3 ,, ,,
2¾″	2 staysail sheets-	- - - -	7½ ,, ,,
2½″	2 vang falls	- - - - -	14 ,, port
			15 ,, starboard
	1 topsail sheet	- - - - -	14 ,,
3″	1 mainsheet	- - - - -	24 ,,
			311 fathoms

TARRED HEMP

Item		Length	No.
13 —2″ stay fall stopper	- - -	2½ fathoms	1
2¼″ standing backstay falls	-	3 ,,	2
2¼″ bowsprit shroud falls	-	3 ,,	2
3″ main shroud lanyards	-	3½ ,,	6

MULE RIGGED MIZZEN

peak brails	- - - -	6 fathoms	1¾″ sisal
main ,,	- - - - - -	8 ,,	2″ tarred hemp
lower ,,	- - - - - -	6 ,,	2″ sisal
peak halyards	- - - -	20 ,,	2¼″ sisal
throat ,,	- - - - - -	18 ,,	2¼″ sisal
sheet fall	- - - - -	10 ,,	2½″ sisal
sheet outhall purchase	- -	10 ,,	2″ sisal
head lacing	- - - -	12 ,,	1⅛″ sisal
boom topping lift purchase	-	4 ,,	2½″ sisal
Bowsprit jib (set flying)			
tack outhaul	- - - -	5 ,,	2¼″ sisal
tack inhaul	- - - -	3 ,,	1½″ sisal
halyard purchase	- - -	5 ,,	2″ sisal
jib sheets	- - - - -	2½ ,, each	2½″ sisal
Stay jib			
halyards	- - - - -	24 ,,	2¼″ sisal
downhaul	- - - -	11 ,,	2″ sisal

WIRE

Average lengths required, standing and running rigging galvanised flex steel for 100-130 ton barges.

Size	Item	Length	No.
$\frac{3}{4}$"	dolly wire - - - - min 50 fathoms - - -		1
$1\frac{1}{4}$"	topsail tack - - - - $3\frac{1}{2}$,, - - - -		1
	main brails - - - - $5\frac{1}{2}$,, each - - -		2
$1\frac{3}{4}$"	topmast stem stay - - - 11 ,, - - - -		1
	,, long ,, - - 16 or 12 with 4 fath. chain tail		1
	,, running back stay - 11 ,, each - - -		2
	,, heel rope - - - $6\frac{1}{2}$,, - - - -		1
	topsail halyard tie - - - 10 ,, - - - -		1
	,, sheet pendant - - $7\frac{1}{2}$,, - - - -		1
	main brail leg - - - - 5 ,, - - - -		1
	rolling vangs - - - $8\frac{1}{2}$—9 fath. each - -		2
	mizzen forestay - - - 2 fathoms - - -		1
	,, shrouds - - - 2 ,, each - - -		4
	,, stanliff - - - 1 ,, - - - -		1
2"	topmast standing back stay - 11 fathoms each - -		2
	main runner leg (to chain leg) $3\frac{1}{2}$,, - - - -		2
	main vangs - - - - 7 ,, ,, - - -		2
	yard tackle pendant - - $5\frac{1}{2}$,, - - - -		1
	bowsprit shrouds (according to length of spar) - - -		2
	jib stay or tack outhaul pendant (according to length of spar)		1
$2\frac{1}{2}$"	stayfall - - - - - 22 fathoms min.		
$3\frac{1}{2}$"	galvanised, iron, for main shrouds and stanliff		
4"	,, ,, ,, fore stay		

Mule rigged

mizzen shrouds - 2"		mizzen sheet outhaul	$1\frac{3}{4}$"
,, iump stay - $1\frac{3}{4}$"		,, vang - -	$1\frac{1}{4}$"
,, boom top lift $1\frac{1}{4}$"			

Bob index continued.

22. A. M. & H. Rankin.
23. Baker (Maldon) Ltd.
24. R. Sully.
25. T. Allsworth.
26. Arthur Gamman Ltd.
27. Anderson & Co.
28. Shaws of Kent.
29. Tester Bros.

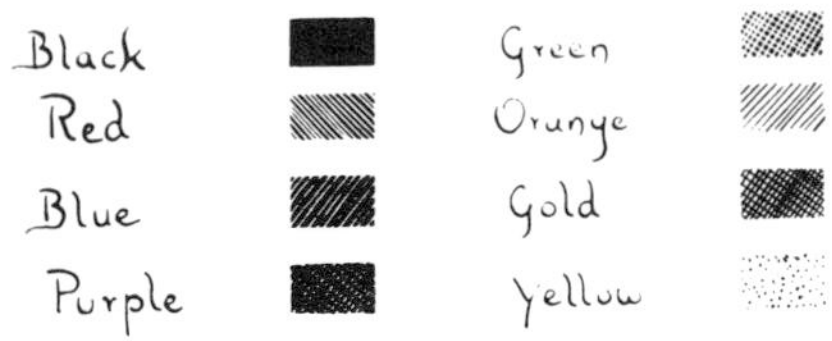
Black
Red
Blue
Purple
Green
Orange
Gold
Yellow

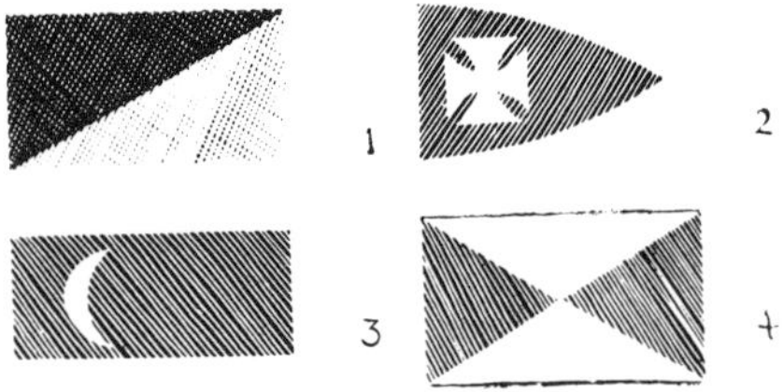
1
2
3
4

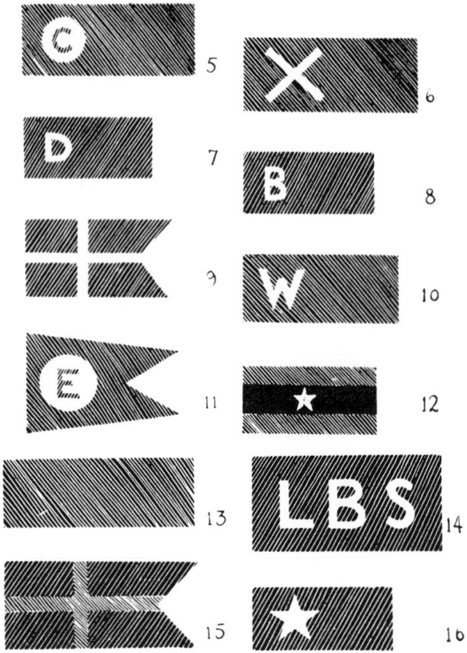
C
5
X
6
D
7
B
8
9
W
10
E
11
12
13
LBS
14
15
16

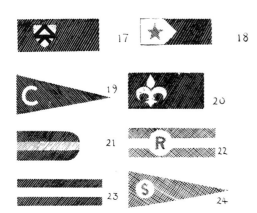

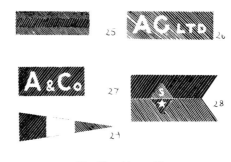

Fig. 63. House Flags.

COMMERCIAL BARGES (active)

SAIL

Name	Built	Owner
Anglia	Ipswich 1898	R. & W. Paul, Ipswich.
Ardeer	Rochester 1895	I.C.I. Ltd.
Ardwina	Ipswich 1909	Daniels Bros., Whitstable.
Asphodel	Rochester 1900	I.C.I. Ltd.
Cambria	Greenhithe 1905	F. T. Everard Ltd., Greenhithe.
Centaur	Harwich 1895	L. & R.T. Co., Strood.
Colonia	Sandwich 1897	Daniels Bros., Whitstable
Dreadnought	Sittingbourne 1907	I.C.I. Ltd.
Edith & Hilda	Milton 1892	I.C.I. Ltd.
Ethel	Harwich 1894	Cranfield Bros., Ipswich
Ethel Ada	Paglesham 1903	I.C.I. Ltd.
George Smeed	Murston 1882	L. & R.T. Co., Strood
Gipping	Ipswich 1889	I.C.I. Ltd.
Kitty	Harwich 1895	L. & R. T. Co., Strood
Lady Maud	Greenhithe 1903	F. T. Everard Ltd., Greenhithe.
Lady Mary	Greenhithe 1900	F. T. Everard Ltd., Greenhithe
Marjorie	Ipswich 1902	R. & W. Paul, Ipswich
May	Harwich 1891	Cranfield Bros., Ipswich

Name	Built	Owner
Memory	Harwich 1904	M. F. Horlock Ltd., Mistley
Millie	Brightlingsea 1892	I.C.I. Ltd.
Mirosa ex Ready	Maldon 1892	L. & R.T. Co., Strood
Nelson	Sittingbourne 1905	Eastwood Ltd., Halstow
Portlight	Mistley 1925	M. F. Horlock, Mistley
Repertor	Mistley 1924	M. F. Horlock, Mistley
Revival ex Eldred		
Watkins	Ipswich 1901	I.C.I. Ltd.
Sara	Conyer 1902	F. T. Everard Ltd., Greenhithe.
Savoy	Rochester 1898	Daniels Bros., Whitstable
Sirdar	Ipswich 1898	L. & R.T. Co., Strood
Spinaway C.	Ipswich 1899	Cranfield Bros., Ipswich
Venture	Ipswich 1900	Cranfield Bros., Ipswich
Veravia	Sittingbourne 1898	
ex Alarm	E. Greenwich (rebuilt)	Shrubshall, Greenwich
Verona	E. Greenwich 1903	Shrubsall, Greenwich
Westmorland	Conyer 1904	Eastwood Ltd., Halstow
Xylonite	Mistley 1926	M. F. Horlock Ltd., Mistley

Total: 34 on the 30th April, 1954.

AUX SAIL

Name	Built	Owner
Alan	Battersea 1900	L. & R.T. Co., Strood
Alaric	Sandwich 1901	L. & R.T. Co., Strood
Beric	Harwich 1896	Cranfield Bros., Ipswich
Beatrice Maud	Sittingbourne 1910	R. Sully, London E.C.
British Empire	Brightlingsea 1899	L. & R.T. Co., Strood
Cabby	Frindsbury 1928	L. & R.T. Co., Strood
Dannebrog	Harwich 1901	Cranfield Bros., Ipswich
Dawn	Maldon 1897	L. & R.T. Co., Strood
Edith	Sittingbourne 1904	Cremer, Faversham
Edith May	Harwich 1906	R. Sully, London, E.C.
Ena	Harwich 1906	R. & W. Paul, Ipswich
Ethel Maud	Maldon 1899	Baker Bros., Maldon

Name	Built	Owner
Felix	Harwich 1893	Cranfield Bros., Ipswich
George & Eliza	Rochester 1907	L. & R.T. Co., Strood
Gladys (Harwich)	Harwich 1901	Cranfield Bros., Ipswich
Glenmore	Rochester 1902	W. R. Cunis, Woolwich
Glenway	Rochester 1913	S. West, Gravesend
Gravelines I ex		
Hilda	Ipswich 1905	R. & W. Paul, Ipswich
Hydrogen	Rochester 1906	R. Sully, London, E.C.
Jock	Ipswich 1908	R. & W. Paul, Ipswich
Kimberley	Harwich 1901	Cranfield Bros., Ipswich
Lady Daphne	Rochester 1923	R. & W. Paul, Ipswich
Lady Helen	Rochester 1902	L. & R.T. Co., Strood
Lady Gwynfred	Gravesend 1904	S. West, Gravesend
Lady Jean	Rochester 1923	R. & W. Paul, Ipswich
Leofleda	Harwich 1914	E. Marriage & Sons, Colchester
Leonard Piper	Greenwich 1910	S. West, Gravesend
Leslie West	Gravesend 1900	L. & R.T. Co., Strood
Lord Roberts	Maldon 1900	A. M. & H. Rankin, Stambridge
Major	Harwich 1897	Anderson, Whitstable
Marie May	Maidstone 1920	L. & R.T. Co., Strood
Nellie Parker	Ipswich 1899	Peter Horlock
Orinoco	E. Greenwich 1895	Cranfield Bros., Ipswich
Oxygen	Rochester 1895	R. Sully, London, E.C.3
Pudge	Rochester 1922	L. & R.T. Co., Strood
Raybel	Sittingbourne	R. Sully, London, E.C.
Redoubtable	Harwich 1915	M. Horlock, Mistley
Remercie	Harwich 1908	M. Horlock, Mistley
Scone	Rochester 1919	L. & R.T. Co., Strood
Thalatta	Harwich 1906	R. & W. Paul, Ipswich
Thyra	Maidstone 1913	L. & R.T. Co., Strood
Tollesbury	Sandwich 1901	R. & W. Paul, Ipswich
Varuna	E. Greenwich 1907	L. & R.T. Co., Strood
Will Everard	Gt. Yarmouth 1925	F. T. Everard Ltd., Greenhithe

Total 44.

MOTOR BARGES

Name	Built	Owner
Arctic	Greenwich 1897	L. & R.T. Co., Strood
Adieu	Mistley 1929	M. F. Horlock, Mistley
Atrato	Wivenhoe 1896	L. & R.T. Co., Strood
Azima	Whitstable 1898	Daniels Bros., Whitstable
British King	Maldon 1901	L. & R.T. Co., Strood
The Brownie	Gravesend 1901	L. & R.T. Co., Strood
C.I.V.	Sittingbourne 1901	T. Allsworth, Queenborough
Celtic	Papendrecht 1903	A. Sheaf, Newport, I.O.W.
Charles Burley	Sittingbourne 1902	C. Burley, Sittingbourne
Clenwood	Borstal 1911	L. & R.T. Co., Strood
Circe	Southampton 1899	L. & R.T. Co., Strood
Coronation	Ipswich 1903	L. & R.T. Co., Strood
Convoy	Rye 1900	R. Sully, London, E.C.
Cygnet	Frindsbury 1881	E. Mumford, Barling, Essex
Dee	Sittingbourne 1898	T. Allsworth, Queenborough
Decima	Southampton 1899	Tester Bros., Greenhithe
Esther	Faversham 1900	Cremer, Faversham
Fred Everard	Gt. Yarmouth 1926	F. T. Everard Ltd., Greenhithe
Greta	Brightlingsea 1892	L. & R.T. Co., Strood
Gazelle ex Runic ex Goldrune	Krimpden D'Ysel 1904	Vectis S.S. Co., Newport, I.O.W.
Gerald	Faversham 1899	Vectis S.S. Co., Newport, I.O.W.
Gwynronald ex Charles Allison	E. Greenwich 1908	S. West, Gravesend
H. T. Willis	Sittingbourne 1889	L. & R.T. Co., Strood
Imperial	E. Greenwich 1902	L. & R.T. Co., Strood
Ironsides	Grays 1900	L. & R.T. Co., Strood
Kathleen	Gravesend 1901	Daniels Bros., Whitstable
King	E. Greenwich 1901	L. & R.T. Co., Strood
Kentish Hoy ex Maymon ex Teutonic	Krimpden D'Ysel 1904	A. Gamman, Chatham
Lais ex Germanic	Krimpden D'Ysel 1904	Finland
Lawson ex Sir Wilfred Lawson	Sittingbourne 1878	Shaws of Kent, Rainham, Kent
M.N.	Rochester 1893	L. & R.T. Co., Strood
Lancashire	Teynham 1900	R. Lapthorn, Hoo, Kent
Maria	Sittingbourne 1898	S. J. Ellis, Sittingbourne
Maid of Connaught ex The Monarch	E. Greenwich 1899	Leigh Building Supply Co.
Maid of Munster ex Bexhill	Sittingbourne 1898	Wakeley Bros., Southwark
Mary Ann	Milton 1900	Mackenzie Gravesend
Mayor	Sandwich 1899	L. & R.T. Co., Strood
Melissa	Southampton 1899	L. & R.T. Co., Strood
Mousme	Maidstone 1924	L. & R.T. Co., Strood
Mildreda	Ipswich 1900	Geo. Andrews (freightage) Ltd., Sittingbourne
Moultonian	Littlehampton 1919	Williams S.S. Co., Southampton
Niagara	Wivenhoe 1898	L. & R.T. Co., Strood
Ninety Nine	Frindsbury 1900	C. Burley, Sittingbourne
Nellie	Faversham 1901	R. Laphorn, Hoo, Kent
Northdown	Whitstable 1924	L. & R.T. Co., Strood
Oceanic	Papendrecht 1902	Vectis S.S. Co., Newport, I.O.W.
Olive May	Sittingbourne 1920	S. West, Gravesend
P.A.M.	Rochester 1900	Wakeley Bros., Southwark
Persevere	Murston 1899	Maynard, Brightlingsea
Pimlico	Borstal 1914	L. & R.T. Co., Strood
Pinup ex Pip	Greenwich 1921	L. & R.T. Co., Strood
Premier	Milton 1900	E. P. Hill, Dover
Pride of Sheppey ex Ethel	Faversham 1900	Geo. Andrews (freightage) Ltd., Sittingbourne
Phoenician	Sittingbourne 1922	R. Sully, London, E.C.
Queen	Sittingbourne 1906	L. & R.T. Co., Strood
R.B.	Rochester 1903	Vectis S.S. Co., Newport, I.O.W.
Raven	Rochester 1904	L. & R.T. Co., Strood
Reminder	Mistley 1929	M. F. Horlock, Mistley
Resourceful	Mistley 1930	M. F. Horlock, Mistley

MOTOR BARGES—*continued*

Name	Built	Owner
Saxon	Southampton 1898	L. & R.T. Co., Strood
Scotsman	Sittingbourne 1899	R. Sully, London, E.C.
Success ex Cymric	Papendrecht 1903	L. & R.T. Co., Strood
Surrey	E. Greenwich 1901	L. & R.T. Co., Strood
Sir Richard	Gravesend 1900	L. & R.T. Co., Strood
Stargate ex Wilfred	E. Greenwich 1926	L. & R.T. Co., Strood
Spartan	Southampton 1898	L. & R.T. Co., Strood
Squawk	Strood 1914	L. & R.T. Co., Strood
Servic	Krimpden D'Ysel 1904	L. & R.T. Co., Strood
Thistle	Port Glasgow 1895	L. & R.T. Co., Strood

Name	Built	Owner
Trilby (Rochester) rebuilt	Sittingbourne 1947	R. Sully, London, E.C.
Trojan	Southampton 1898	A. Johnson, Sheerness
Virocca	Southampton 1899	Shaws of Kent, Rainham
Vicunia	E. Greenwich 1912	Daniels Bros., Whitstable
Victor	Ipswich 1895	L. & R.T. Co., Strood
Victory	Conyer 1901	T. Schmidt, Queenborough
Vigilant	Ipswich 1904	L. & R.T. Co., Strood
Viking	Rochester 1895	L. & R.T. Co., Strood
Water Lily	Rochester 1902	Wakeley Bros., Southwark
Windward	Sittingbourne 1897	Wakeley Bros., Southwark
Westall	Strood 1913	L. & R.T. Co., Strood
Wyvenhoe	Wivenhoe 1898	L. & R.T. Co., Strood
Wessex	Littlehampton 1912	Williams S.S. Co., Southampton

Total 82, April 30th, 1954.

LIST OF OWNERS

	Sail	Aux.	M.B.
Imperial Chemical Industries Ltd.	8	—	—
London & Rochester Trading Co. Ltd.	5	13	36
Cranfield Bros., Ipswich	4	5	—
Daniels Bros., Whitstable	3	1	2
M. F. Horlock, Mistley	4	2	3
F. T. Everard, Greenhithe	4	1	1
Cremer & Others, Faversham	—	1	1
Shrubshall, East Greenwich	2	—	—
R. & W. Paul, Ipswich	2	7	—
Wakeley Bros., Southwark	—	—	4
Eastwood Ltd., Lower Halstow	2	—	—
Raymond Sully, London, E.C.	—	5	4
Samuel West Ltd., Gravesend	—	3	2
Marriage & Sons, Colchester	—	1	—
A. M. & H. Rankin, Stambridge, Essex	—	1	—
Anderson, Whitstable	—	1	—
W. R. Cunis Ltd., South Woolwich	—	1	—
A. Sheaf, Newport, I.O.W.	—	—	1
Vectis, S.S. Co., Newport, I.O.W.	—	—	4
A. Sheaf, Newport, I.O.W.	—	—	1
Williams, S.S. Co., Southampton	—	—	2
T. Allsworth, Queenborough	—	—	2
E. Mumford, Barling, Essex	—	—	1
Shaws of Kent	—	—	2
T. Schmidt, Queenborough	—	—	1
R. Lapthorn, Hoo, Kent	1	—	4
Mackenzie, Gravesend	—	—	1
A. Johnson, Sheerness	—	—	1
C. Burley, Sittingbourne	—	—	2

	Sail	Aux.	M.B.
A. Gamman, Chatham - - - -	—	—	1
Tester Bros., Greenhithe - - - -	—	—	1
E. P. Hill, Dover - -. - - -	—	—	1
'Lais', Finland - - - - -	—	—	1
S. J. Ellis, Sittingbourne - - - -	—	—	1
Baker Bros., Maldon - - - -	—	1	—

	Sail	Aux.	M.B.
Leigh Building Supply Co. Ltd. - -	—	—	1
Maynard, Brightlingsea - - - -	—	—	1
Peter Horlock - - - - - -	—	1	—
	36	47	80

INDEX
(NAMES OF BARGES)

Other Adlard Coles titles of interest

Barges: John Leather
ISBN 0 229 11594 2
This classic, beautifully illustrated survey of barges covers British, North American and New Zealand sailing barges. Using high quality illustrations, John Leather authoritatively traces the history of barges, how they were worked in rivers and along the coasts and how they were adapted to local or changing conditions.

Gaff Rig, Second Edition: John Leather
ISBN 0 229 11844 5
Gaff rig is now enjoying a considerable revival, and in this new edition of John Leather's definitive study he examines both the history of gaff rigged craft and the practical aspects of handling them. Two new chapters survey French and Baltic rigs and the more technical details of the vessels, their working practices and the characters who sailed them are interspersed with humour and anecdotes.

'A good book, exhaustive in its study of the subject and with clear, easy to follow line drawings and photographs.' *Sea Spray*

Spritsails and Lugsails: John Leather
ISBN 0 229 11517 9
In this third book in John Leather's historical sail trilogy the author evokes tales of a hundred years ago as he traces the evolution of two of the world's oldest rigs. The book is illustrated with the author's own drawings and many rare photographs of these craft.

For a complete catalogue of Adlard Coles titles write to: Adlard Coles, 8 Grafton Street, London W1X 3LA